MRS DAR
HEALIN

A Magickal Journey of Healing Through the Senses

MRS DARLEY'S PAGAN HEALING WISDOM

A Magickal Journey of Healing Through the Senses

Carole Carlton

First edition
Published in Great Britain
By Mirage Publishing 2011

First published in paperback 2011

A CIP catalogue record for this book
Is available from the British Library.

ISBN: 978-1-90257-8767

Mirage Publishing
PO Box 161
Gateshead
NE8 4WW
Great Britain

Printed and bound in Great Britain by

Book Printing UK
Remus House, Coltsfoot Drive, Woodston, Peterborough, PE2 9JX, UK

Layout by Artistic Director Sharon Anderson

Papers used in the production of this book are recycled,
thus reducing environmental depletion.

In memory of Mum; with love.

Contents

Introduction: The Secret of Healing 9

Chapter 1: The Nature of Disease and the Mind, Body, Spirit Connection 19
Chapter 2: The Subtle Energy Fields 59
Chapter 3: The Senses 95
Chapter 4: The Sense of Touch 109
Chapter 5: The Sense of Smell 135
Chapter 6: The Sense of Taste 171
Chapter 7: The Sense of Hearing 209
Chapter 8: The Sense of Sight 253
Chapter 9: Becoming Whole 289

Other titles 299

Disclaimer

Disclaimer: the entire contents of this book are based upon research conducted by the author, unless otherwise noted. The publisher, the author, the distributors and bookstores present this information for educational purposes only. Any exercises presented here, either physical or mental, are to be practiced with caution. Should you experience any discomfort or trauma from any of the processes involved you are advised to stop. This information is not intended to diagnose or prescribe for medical or psychological conditions or to claim to prevent, treat, mitigate or cure such conditions. The author and the publisher are not making an attempt to recommend specific products as treatment of disease, and neither do they have any financial interest in the sale of the substances described in this book. In presenting this information, no attempt is being made to provide diagnosis, care, treatment or rehabilitation of individuals, or apply medical, mental health or human development principles, to provide diagnosing, treating, operating or prescribing for any human disease, pain, injury, deformity or physical condition. The information contained herein is not intended to replace a one-on-one relationship with a doctor or qualified health care professional. Therefore, the reader should be made aware that this information is not intended as medical advice, but rather a sharing of knowledge and information from the research and experience of the author. The publisher and the author encourage you to make your own health care decisions based upon your research and in partnership with a qualified health care professional. You and only you are responsible if you choose to do anything based on what you read.

Introduction

The Secret of Healing

The Gift
'Cure us,' called the lepers.
'Help us,' begged the blind.
'Save us,' said the sick.

Mend us?' asked the lame.

'The gift of healing is already yours,' She said.

The Invitation
To understand how to heal, we have to come to truly know ourselves from the outside in and from the inside out; a task that most of us would tend to shy away from.

I often wonder how many of us know who we are deep down, at the level of the soul. The answer, I suspect, is very few, for the majority of us are quite content to bumble along through life, occasionally not feeling particularly happy, but simply content to accept that that is the way things are.

Sometimes we receive a wake up call from the universe, telling us that something is amiss and we are not fulfilling our true potential. That call can come through illness, divorce, redundancy and a myriad of other life crises, but what we need to remember is that each one of these comes as a friend; a friend that encourages us to overhaul our lives and hopefully make the changes that will put us in touch with our true life's purpose.

Life has given me several alarm calls, each one increasingly louder than the last in the hope, no doubt, that one day I would finally wake up and become conscious as to whom I really am and the direction in which I should be going.

Following one such call in the early 1990s, I moved to Cornwall in order to make a fresh start and it was there, whilst living amongst the wild landscape of Bodmin Moor, that Mrs Darley came into my life.

As my Cornish life unfolded, I became immersed in the mysterious and magickal[1] world of my wise and enigmatic next door neighbour, who taught me things that were far removed from the mundane tasks of daily life. She told stories that broadened my horizons, made comments that challenged my thought patterns and, through her insight, often exposed my numb and dormant feelings.

Her knowledge of the ancient festivals, the Moon and the natural world, made me appreciate our beautiful planet and helped me to understand that a Divine essence is present in every aspect of our daily lives. Her teachings, which often involved an eclectic mix of her delightful friends, were always shrouded in mystery, and my brief sojourns into the magickal realms both fascinated and frightened me.

Following several periods of less than robust health, Mrs Darley invited me to undertake a healing journey

---

[1] Magick is an Early Modern English spelling for magic, it is used to differentiate between the spiritual and stage magic.

with regards to both my physical body and my life and, considering this an opportunity too precious to miss, I readily agreed.

It was a journey, however, that would not only make me view life and death in a different way, but would also alter the way in which I interacted with my body and ultimately become a journey that changed my career and touched my soul.

Understanding the Meaning of Healing

This book is a signpost to the healing gifts of the Universe that are available to each and every one of us. Nothing in this world should, or indeed can, be looked at in isolation, for everything is connected and interconnected. We are all part of the whole and, therefore, what we do to ourselves we do to each other. As a result, what we think, feel, say and do affects our overall health and the health of those around us.

This book aims to explore the many levels upon which healing can take place, from the physical and emotional, to the psychological and spiritual. It investigates healing from the inside out and from the outside in, with particular emphasis on the importance of the senses in the whole process.

It is, of course, impossible to mention every type of healing modality within this book, but what is within aims to give suggestions and directions as to where help may be found. Ultimately, however, as Mrs Darley gently points out, the power to heal already lies within each and every one of us.

The word 'healing' is an extremely evocative one, but what exactly does it mean? The verb 'to heal, the dictionary tells us, is: *to become sound or healthy again, to make whole.* A description with which the majority of us, no doubt, would agree. However, very few of us actually understand how to truly heal ourselves once disease takes hold.

Most of us are far more familiar with the verb 'to cure', as this is often associated with the medical profession; the respected body to whom the masses turn in the first instance when illness strikes. The dictionary definition of the verb 'to cure' is: *to relieve the symptoms of a disease or condition.* Meaning that we undertake a course of recommended treatment until the symptoms disappear.

In our language today, the words 'cure' and 'healing' have almost become synonymous with each other and are considered by many to mean one and the same thing - the transformation from a state of ill health to one of wellness. In reality however the two words are worlds apart in their meaning:

To Cure

A cure, in the eyes of the medical profession, is said to have occurred when the progression of a physical illness has been successfully stopped through the treatment of the symptom.

This does not necessarily mean, however, that the negative emotional and psychological issues, which often underpin that illness have been dealt with and, as a result, it is probable that either the same illness will reappear or another occur.

The process of curing is a passive one. It can be likened to dropping a car off at the garage for a repair and picking it up when everything is done, thereby taking no active part in the curing process other than handing total control over to the medical profession.

To Heal

Healing is an interactive process, often involving both the patient and a medical professional, and is one which asks us to reassess all aspects of our life.

Sadly, a physical healing is not always possible, for death is an inevitable part of life. That does not mean, however, that we are prevented from healing on an emotional, psychological or spiritual level.

It is a matter of personal preference as to whether we opt for the detached 'cure' or the more interactive 'healing'. For in matters of health, as in all aspects of life, we always have a choice. In the words of Albert Einstein:

'There are two ways to live your life. One is as though nothing is a miracle. The other is as though everything is a miracle.'

Mrs Darley Tale: The Accident

'Are you alright, dear?' Mrs Darley's voice broke into my thoughts as I sat on the step of my porch with a cup of coffee. 'I wondered whether I should disturb you as you looked miles away.'

I turned to her and smiled. 'Yes I'm OK, just a little shaken up that's all.'

'Why, my dear, whatever has happened?'

'I saw a really bad accident this morning on my way to work; a head on. A young lad overtook three of us on a blind bend and a lorry was coming the other way. He was killed outright. While we were waiting to give statements to the police I got talking to a man who was a passenger in one of the cars in front of me. He said he knew the lad, Adam I think he said his name was, as they lived in the same street. Apparently Adam's home life was very unhappy, an absent father, a drunken mother and an abusive step-father. I couldn't get the accident and this lad's unhappy life off my mind all day, perhaps something had upset him, perhaps….' the sentence tailed off as I felt my eyes welling with tears.

Mrs Darley walked over to me and, taking my hand, pulled me up from the step. 'Come along, dear,' she said, 'I think you're in need of something a little stronger than a cup of coffee.'

I followed her into her cottage and within minutes was ensconced in my favourite fireside chair. The obligatory whisky followed, but to my surprise it was hot!

'There,' said Mrs Darley settling herself opposite me, 'the hot whisky will steady your nerves and the spices within will give you strength.'

I smiled. 'Thank you,' I said, 'that's just what I need. Mind you, here I am feeling sorry for myself, when it's Adam's family who must be suffering. What a waste of a young life. It makes you wonder why such things have to happen. It all seems so cruel … so pointless somehow.'

'Is that what you think?' asked Mrs Darley.

'Well yes … wouldn't that be most people's reaction to such a tragedy?'

Mrs Darley nodded. 'Yes, it would certainly be most people's reaction.'

I looked at her, 'I can feel a "but" coming.'

She smiled. 'But just because most people might think that way, does that automatically mean it's right?'

'Well no, but in this instance I think it's an understandable human reaction.'

'No one is denying, my dear, that from a human point of view, the loss of a young life is very sad, especially for parents, partners and friends. However, what we often forget, or perhaps choose to ignore, is that life here in this human form is fleeting, although it does provide us with a myriad of experiences through which the soul can grow.

'You mentioned that this young man's home life was not particularly happy, well perhaps he needed to experience that unhappiness for many reasons.'

'Like what?' I asked. 'Who would choose to experience unhappiness and possible abuse?'

'No one on a conscious level,' Mrs Darley replied, 'but many of our life experiences are chosen long before we incarnate into our physical body. Perhaps this young man needed to know what abuse felt like in order that he would never inflict it on another. On the other hand, he may have been settling a karmic debt, which has spilled into this life from a life past, or he may have unselfishly given up his life in order that his parents may learn from his death.'

'Why? What can his parents possibly learn from his death?'

'In order to change, some people have to experience loss and pain. Look at the two warring families in Romeo and Juliet. It took the death of their children to bring them to their senses and realise the futility of their dispute. We can only hope that the death of Adam will be a wake up call for his family and perhaps prevent them from treating anyone else in the same manner.

'On the other hand, of course, his death may not have been for any of these reasons. Perhaps the distress he was feeling was so great that he could never see a time when he would experience solace or love, and so he chose what we would consider to be an untimely death ... to act as the ultimate healer.'

'Are you saying he killed himself on purpose?' I asked.

'Again, I will use the phrase "not consciously", but perhaps his Higher Self, that deeper, all knowing part, knew that this was the only way to bring about true healing.'

'But we never associate death with healing,' I said, 'in fact it's probably the opposite; death is seen as a failure to heal.'

Mrs Darley nodded. 'But that's just consensus truth, the belief of the masses. It doesn't have to become your own personal truth.'

I sat in silence musing for a moment or two. After a lengthy pause, Mrs Darley gave more meaning to her words. 'You see, my dear, what we often fail to remember is that we are primarily spiritual beings, dressed in human form and, therefore, death is merely a vehicle in which the soul journeys home.'

'But if we're just returning home, why bother incarnating into human form in the first place, why don't we just remain in spirit?'

'Because becoming human provides us with physical pain and delights, emotional highs and lows, mental euphoria and anguish, spiritual bliss and confusion and yet, for all the soul understands these things in concept, it still needs to experience them for itself and it is the physical incarnation that allows that.'

Mrs Darley looked at me and smiled. 'Just as a young seed cannot grow in mid air but has to be planted in the earth, so your soul cannot grow on the spiritual plane, but has to be planted within a physical body.'

'I've never thought about life and death in that way,' I said, 'death has always been the enemy, never the ally.'

'And that, my dear, is what we are led to believe. Admittedly, our life here on Earth is precious and forms a valuable part of our soul experience, however this earthly life comprises only a small part of our overall existence and, when our work here is complete for a particular incarnation, death merely comes as a friend to light the path that leads us home.'

The Ribboned Path

The ribboned path is endless,
Melting into sunlit days,
Calling me to dance anew
The wild adventure of life.

The ribboned path is shorter,
Thinning into midday haze.
I stop and reassess
The wild adventure of life.

The ribboned path is ending,
Fading into darkening woods
Yet I emerge, and dance again
The wild adventure of life.

Chapter 1

The Nature of Disease and the Mind, Body, Spirit Connection

The Search
Purveyors of health,
Of tablets and potions,
Of ointment and pills,
Of ideas and notions.
Advisors of health,
From doctors and nurses,
To shamans and healers,
With blessings and curses.

Yet health must be sought
Through the realms of the mind,
Through the peace of the spirit
For there you will find,
The will to make changes,
The will to be whole,
The will to find healing
To set free your soul.

Mrs Darley Tale: The Labyrinth

'Well, dears, it's finally finished!' Mrs Darley announced as she appeared from the kitchen with a tray of glasses and Pimms, closely followed by Phyllis who was carrying some rather delicious scones and clotted cream.

'What is?' Rose asked.

'The labyrinth,' Mrs Darley replied.

'Oh, yes,' said Rose, 'I remember now, isn't it a friend of yours, Phyllis, who's been making it for what seems like forever?'

Phyllis nodded as she put the scones down on the table. 'Yes, after nearly two summers in the making, Michael says it's finally ready for guests.'

'Then we must all go,' said Mrs Darley.

'Well I'm free anytime,' said Rose, 'how about Tuesday?'

'We must do it when everyone can come,' said Mrs Darley looking at me, 'don't forget, some of us are at work.'

'Oh, don't mind me,' I said quickly, secretly wondering why the sudden appearance of a labyrinth had caused so much excitement, after all it was only a maze; just kids stuff really.

'Oh, no, dear,' said Mrs Darley, 'you must come. It's something I want you to see and besides,' she added, 'I think it will do you good.'

Wondering how on earth a labyrinth would do me good was quite beyond my comprehension. However, with this comment, the conversation ended and a date was set for the following Saturday.

Saturday morning dawned bright and clear and rather reluctantly I dutifully called for Mrs Darley and Rose and we set off for the pretty market town of Tavistock, just over the Devon border. From here we left civilization behind and began to climb eastward out of the town and up onto the wild and barren land of Dartmoor.

'I'm glad it's a nice day,' said Rose as we wove our way across a ribbon of road, bordered by the vast expanse of the moor. 'Dartmoor always gives me the creeps; it's not friendly like our Bodmin Moor.'

'All moors can be bleak at times, my dear,' said Mrs Darley, 'just like life, but when the sun comes out like today there is nothing more breathtaking than to find yourself in a magnificent wild landscape, which serves to remind all of us of our timeless connection to the earth.'

Her words made me smile and, for the first time since this rather unusual outing had been arranged, I actually began to look forward to the day ahead. A further ten minutes into our journey, Mrs Darley indicated that I turn down a well rutted track, where we plunged deep into a wooded valley that followed the twists and turns of a moorland stream.

'Here we are, dear, you can park anywhere in this yard,' Mrs Darley said as I pulled alongside a dozen or so other cars.

'I thought this was just a maze in someone's garden,' I said to Mrs Darley as we began to walk towards a crowd of people who were congregating on the other side of a five barred gate.

'Well, it is on private property,' said Mrs Darley, 'but I think they've got quite a few acres so I expect it will be quite large. Oh, and it's a labyrinth, dear, not a maze.'

'Ah,' I said, 'I didn't realise there was a difference'

'Well that's understandable,' Mrs Darley replied, 'I don't suppose many people do realise there's a difference and these days the terms have become almost synonymous with each other. For the record though, a maze is full of dead ends, although you can reach the centre through much trial and error. A labyrinth on the other hand only has one pathway to its centre.'

As I was taking on board this new piece of information, I was delighted to see Phyllis hurrying forward and beckoning us through the gate. After the usual affectionate greetings we joined what looked like twenty or so other people and followed them around the end of an old barn. As we turned the corner, we were overshadowed by the most imposing tor and at its foot, carved into the grassland of the moor, was the most enormous labyrinth.

'Wow,' I murmured.

'Isn't it stunning?' Rose whispered, 'now I can see why it took two summers to carve out.'

'The plan is, to let someone in every couple of minutes and in that way everyone will have their own space in which to walk,' said Phyllis.

'We've got to walk it?' I asked, 'but why?'

'Because it's a meditative journey,' said Mrs Darley.

'I don't understand,' I said.

'You will,' she replied, 'come on, let's join the queue.'

My turn came all too quickly and I soon found myself passing through the little gate that heralded the beginning of my journey. I felt rather self-conscious at first, knowing that the remainder of the queue was watching me take my first tentative steps around the carved path.

As I walked, I began to find the whole experience slightly hypnotic, moving out time and time again to the edge of the labyrinth before being brought tantalisingly close to the centre and, for once, I thought of nothing other than following the path.

After a few minutes, however I became aware of people walking towards me. They had obviously found the centre and were now winding their way back and, much to my disappointment, I found my trancelike state broken by the fact that I had to stop and give way. Eventually I reached the centre and spent a few moments reflecting on a journey that would only have taken me a minute to walk in a straight line, yet which had taken a good ten minutes via the labyrinth.

'And how did you find your experience?' asked Mrs Darley as we sat at a table while Rose went to fetch coffee from the barn.

'Very thought provoking,' I said, 'although I must admit, I couldn't really see the point at first, but as I began to walk, I seemed to forget about everything else.'

'Until you met people coming back the other way?' said Mrs Darley.

I looked at her and smiled, 'Well, yes, I did find that rather disruptive.'

'Walking a labyrinth, my dear, is not only a meditative experience it is also a teaching tool. You see it is easy to be at peace with ourselves when we have no outside influences, no obstacles to overcome, but it is when we have to deal with those outside influences that we learn most about who we really are.'

I nodded, 'Yes, I can see that.'

'I watched you for a few minutes, until it was my time to enter the labyrinth,' she said.

'Oh, dear, that doesn't bode well,' I smiled.

'Not at all,' she said, 'I saw a young woman who, when undertaking a task, becomes totally focussed and that is to be commended. However, when others stepped across your path, that's when I noticed your submissive nature. You were always the first to give way, to stop what you were doing and let others continue uninterrupted.'

'Is that so wrong?' I asked.

'Not wrong, my dear, no, but there has to be give and take in all aspects of life, otherwise your reserves become depleted. You become like the lake whose water only flows outward, leaving you parched and dry.'

'It's the way I've been brought up,' I said, 'to be polite.'

'There's a difference, my dear, between being polite and being taken advantage of. I watched a young man who walked the labyrinth just ahead of us. He smiled and nodded to everyone whom he met along the path and, as a result, many stood aside to let him pass. Occasionally of course, he stepped aside for others, but that was his choice. You see, my dear, we should greet others with quiet confidence and in so doing; our lives will maintain their equilibrium.'

'The relationship I had before I came here, it wasn't healthy. I allowed myself to be controlled. I was afraid.'

'And so your reserves have run dry,' said Mrs Darley quietly, 'perhaps, my dear, it is time to let your lake refill.'

Understanding the Nature of Disease

This chapter focuses on the importance of the mind,

body, spirit connection in the healing process and endeavours to explain why it is necessary to attend to all aspects of the Self in order to achieve and maintain optimum health. Before we can have a real understanding of health however, we have to have an appreciation of the nature of disease.

We are so adept at apportioning blame to outside influences for the state of our health that we have almost become masters of the art.

- There's a nasty bug going around.
- Everyone has a cold at the moment.
- It's the weather.

We are all aware that germs and viruses cause disease, but is it a foregone conclusion that just because a virus is 'doing the rounds' we will have to catch it? The answer to this question lies in a claim made by a nineteenth century French Physiologist called Claude Bernard, who challenged Louis Pasteur's beliefs that microbes alone are responsible for disease.

Bernard's theory stated that unless the body provided the microbes with just the right conditions in which to live (i.e. a lowered immune system), they could not survive and concluded that lowered resistance, rather than germs, was the significant factor in the manifestation of disease.

In order to prove Bernard's claims, a Bavarian chemist called Max von Pettenkofer performed a rather dramatic test. In October 1892, he took cholera bacteria from a man called Robert Knoch, mixed it in a glass of water and drank it. His students, who witnessed the experiment, expected the worst, however all Pettenkofer experienced during the days that followed was a mild case of diarrhoea.

The 1960 Australian Nobel Prize winner in the field of immunology, Sir Macfarlane Burnett, discovered that within our bodies there can be as many as 100,000 cells becoming cancerous each day, but a healthy immune system will ensure they are destroyed as a matter of course.

It is, therefore, important to have an appreciation of the miracle that is our immune system before we learn how to ensure it remains as healthy as possible.

The Immune System

The body's protection against outside intrusion runs like a high security operation and has two forms of defence: non-specific and specific. Non-specific defence is designed first and foremost to keep intruders out, but if they do manage to break in, then the specific immune response leaps into action in order to detect the invader and deal with it as soon as possible.

Non-Specific Immune Defence

There are four types of non-specific immune defence (innate):

1. The skin forms the first line of defence and provides a solid barrier, which germs find difficult to penetrate. If however there are cuts or lesions on the skin's surface, this form of defence becomes weakened.
2. Mucous membranes in the nasal, respiratory and digestive tracts attempt to stop germs from entering the body by trapping microbes in the

natural mucous adhesive.

3. The stomach, with its high hydrochloric acid content, attempts to preserve its sterility by destroying all bacterial toxins.
4. The body produces certain antimicrobial substances including interferon, complement and properdin, which attempt to reduce the virulence of viruses, triggering inflammatory responses and destroying certain types of bacteria.

Specific Immune Defence

The specific immune defence system involves the production of a specific antibody to destroy a particular antigen.

Under a microscope, a drop of blood should comprise of ninety nine percent red blood cells and one percent white cells. It is the white blood cells that form the security guards of the immune system, with different jobs assigned to each member.

Two specific types of white cells exist within this security team, both of which initially form in the liver of the embryo before birth and then move to the bone marrow.

Half of these cells, known as the 'B' cells (bone marrow derived), remain in the bone marrow, while the other half move to the thymus gland where they are referred to as T cells (thymus derived).

B Cells

The B cells produce antibodies to neutralise each antigen or foreign invader, including: germs, viruses, pollen, fungi, chemicals, dust or anything which triggers an immune response.

T Cells
There are four types of T cells:

1. The Killer T Cell:
These cells are equipped with an arsenal which is able to damage or kill cells that harbour a foreign organism. They do this by secreting a substance that attracts macrophages (large white blood cells) to the site of invasion where they can destroy the antigens by ingesting the offending cell.

2. The Helper T Cell
These are the scout cells that sound the alarm as soon as they recognise a foreign invader.

3. The Suppressor T Cell
These are known as the 'immunoregulatory cells' and can be referred to as the senior security guards which are in charge of the intensity and the duration of the battle carried out by the attacking cells. They also are responsible for restraining the uncontrollable urge of the killer cells.

4. The Delayed Hypersensitivity Producing T Cell
Once activated (which can take up to forty eight hours), these delayed hypersensitivity producing T cells call the macrophages for help by secreting chemicals that attract the macrophages to assist in the battle.

The ratio of T suppressor cells to T helper cells is a good indicator of the health of the immune system. Normally the ratio is 1.8 helper cells to each suppressor cell. Too many suppressor cells means that the immune system is being switched off and AIDS patients, for example, often show a ratio of 1:1 or less.

It therefore becomes easy to appreciate Claude Bernard's theory that if this highly efficient system is in perfect working order, germs and viruses will find it very difficult to penetrate, let alone survive within the human body. So how does the immune system become weakened enough to let illnesses take hold?

Understanding why we become Ill and the Triggers for Stress

Most people today would agree that stress plays an important factor in the onset of many diseases and it is estimated that of all illnesses reported to GP's, seventy five percent are stress related.

In 1958, research at McGill University, in the USA, revealed that thirty five out of forty patients suffering from multiple sclerosis had been under prolonged stress before their illness manifested, and relapses usually followed on the heels of renewed stress.

Being under stress however does not necessarily mean that a life threatening illness will materialise, for stress can be responsible for anything from the common cold to a nervous breakdown.

On a more positive note, stress can have a positive side and *'eustress'*, or short term stress, is actually good for us. This is the type of controlled stress that gives us the competitive edge and makes us perform to our full potential on occasions when we may feel nervous, such as when we have to perform in public, take a driving test or sit an exam.

This is due to the fact that three major hormones are released into the blood stream each of which has commendable functions:

1. **Cortisol** enhances immune system activity, reduces inflammation, helps wounds to heal and reduces allergic responses.

2. **Adrenaline** dilates the airways of the lungs to enable air to flow more easily, allows the oxygen carrying capacity of the blood to be increased and stimulates the spleen into releasing red blood cells from its store.

3. **Noradrenalin** enhances mental alertness, heightens sensory activity, i.e. the pupils of the eyes increase in size to allow more light in and therefore improve vision. Hearing becomes more acute and the skin becomes more sensitive to touch.

However, when stress is prolonged, these hormones constantly flow around the bloodstream in excessive amounts and can begin to have profound detrimental effects on our general health. It is at this point that signs and symptoms begin to show, on a physical, behavioural, and psychological level.

Level on which disorder manifests	**Possible disorders**
Physical	Heart disease - angina – hyper-tension – Stroke – migraine – indigestion – nausea – heartburn – ulcers – ulcerative colitis – irritable bowel – diarrhoea – constipation – flatulence – headaches – cramps – muscular spasm – back pain – neck pain – diabetes – cancer – rheumatoid arthritis – allergies – asthma – colds and flu – sexual disorders – skin disorders – sleep disorders

Behavioural	Overeating – obesity – loss of appetite – anorexia – increase in smoking, caffeine intake, alcohol consumption, recreational drugs.
Psychological	Anxiety – fear – phobias – obsessions - depression

Table 1.1

Stress means many things to many people and everyone's stress levels are different, as are the reasons for becoming stressed. Any of the following can cause stress:

- Own behaviour
- Relationships
- Work
- Finance
- Noise
- Pollution
- Traffic
- Family
- Environment
- Boredom
- Illness of self
- Illness of others
- Lack of love
- Loneliness
- Negative thinking

Perhaps it is too simple a solution to think that if we were just able to remove the stress from our lives then we would automatically regain our health. It has to be said, however, that the ability to maintain our health and well-being is often less straight forward than it might initially appear and there are some instances when illness itself has benefits.

The Benefits of becoming Ill

It is perhaps an alien thought that we are able to create illness, albeit on a subconscious level in order that we may benefit in some way, but Dr Carl Simonton, a leading American oncologist, acknowledges five main benefits of becoming ill:

1. Illness provides us with permission to get out of dealing with a troublesome problem or situation.
2. Illness ensures attention, care, and nurturing from people around us.
3. Illness allows us to have breathing space in which to gather energy, or to deal with an existing problem.
4. Illness provides us with an incentive for personal growth, or to give up a habit.
5. Illness means not having to meet our own or other people's expectations.

Many years ago, when I was sixteen, my father became very ill with a carbuncle, the like of which, doctors at the local hospital said, had not been documented since the First World War. He had to have a total of three months away from work and was collected every day by ambulance to have medical treatment, eventually leading to a skin graft.

During this time he gave up cigarettes, a habit which had led him to smoking at least forty a day and, as he gradually regained his strength, he began to enjoy his garden again, something that working six and a half days a week left him very little time to do. Eventually he returned to work, stronger and healthier than he had been for years.

For some, though, the benefits of becoming ill far outweigh those of being well and for people with that mindset, little can be done to restore health unless a greater benefit can be found. In this way, many people can be said to collude with the agents of disease by providing bacteria, viruses and carcinogens, with a fertile terrain in which to settle and thrive, thereby playing their part in the creation of a disease or illness.

Understanding the Mind, Body, Spirit Connection

When illness strikes, whether it is in the form of the common cold or something more serious, the majority of us will react in the same way and ask, 'How can I be rid of these symptoms?' We will then wage war on the illness and throw every weapon we possibly can at it, from aspirin to major surgery. Although all of these are understandable responses, there are two important questions that we should ask as we begin our attack:

1. Why has this illness manifested?
2. What is it trying to say to me?

It is agreed in most modalities of complementary health care, that in order for good health to prevail, it is simply not enough to pay attention to the physical body alone. In many cases, both health and disease begin and end with what is happening on a psychological, emotional and spiritual level.

When we experience ill health we should, in addition to seeking a physical cure, also explore the deeper reason behind its appearance and look to make the changes in our lives that will enable us to restore harmony on all levels. In this way we will be ascribing to the principal of holistic health, which aims to, 'make whole' and derives from the Greek word of the same meaning; *'holos'*.

'The cure of the part should not be attempted without the treatment of the whole, and also no attempt should be made to cure the body without the soul, and therefore if the head and body are to be well you must begin by curing the mind: that is the first thing ... for it is the error of our day in the treatment of the human body, that physicians separate the soul from the body.'

- Plato

How sad that thousands of years after those words were first written, nothing has really changed and many of us still rely solely upon the medical profession when we become ill, rather than taking an active part in the recovery process through changing areas in our life that cause us anxiety or pain.

Being human is a complex matter and achieving holism - that the whole is greater than the sum of its parts - is, without doubt, a difficult task to accomplish. It involves taking time out to assess and reassess our changing needs as life progresses, a task many of us tend to push aside as we bumble through our daily tasks, often lurching from one health crisis to another. However, we would not consider putting a new car on the road and expect it to run for its lifespan without ever assessing its needs ... human life is no different.

In order, therefore, for the human body to be healthy there has to be balance and harmony in every aspect of life as the following equation illustrates:

BALANCE + HARMONY = EASE
IMBALANCE + DISHARMONY =DIS-EASE

How then can we set about achieving an overall state of ease and, as a consequence, obtain and maintain health?

The Aspects of Holism

We often hear the term, 'mind, body, spirit' bandied around to refer to something ethereal and otherworldly, yet these are the precise components that we must look at if we wish to achieve and maintain health.

Although these subjects are almost inexhaustible, an attempt will be made in the remainder of this chapter to provide a flavour of each and their importance in our overall health.

Honouring the Spirit

The terms 'soul' and 'spirit' mean different things to different people and although I learned from Mrs Darley that, from her point of view, they had very different meanings, for the purpose of this book, the words are interchangeable.

When using the term 'spirituality', I am not referring to a particular religious order, or doctrine. Spirituality encompasses many things, from walking in the woods and appreciating nature, to spending a quiet moment cultivating a personal relationship with a Divine essence, regardless of its form.

Spirituality involves having the ability to see the bigger picture and exploring the reasons for being here. It is about following a path that resonates with who we really are and about questioning and reassessing our choices. It is about being open-minded to all paths and modes of thought and then, and only then, deciding what we think and what we want, rather than accepting what parents, teachers, the church or significant others have taught us.

It is frightening to see just how many people suffer from ill health because they are guilt ridden about ideas and beliefs which were instilled into them as child. As an adult they may not wish to adhere to these beliefs, but still feel as though they should, even though they don't really understand the 'why'.

The soul is the still, small voice that whispers to us in our quieter moments, through our dreamtime, through methods of divination, or during deep meditation. The soul often tells us what we've always known, but because acknowledging it means that either we, or some aspect of our life, would have to change, we choose to ignore it and banish it deep within. The voice of the soul though cannot be silenced and we choose to ignore it at our peril.

When the soul speaks to us, it does so with such depth of feeling, with such heartfelt longing that once we have heard it, there can be no mistaking it. This isn't a whim or a passing fancy, but a yearning that always seems to have been present, and when we make a decision at a soul level, it seems so right that we simply accept it without question. When we listen to the soul, life becomes magickal.

Sadly, our conscious mind likes to be the boss when it comes to decision making and we often let the soul remain unheard simply because we don't know how to listen to its silent plea.

In order to achieve a state of harmony between what we really need in our lives and what we think we need, we have to create a relaxing space where the conscious mind of our daily waking lives and the sub-conscious mind, the messenger of our soul, can communicate.

Many of us may think that we are capable of entering this sufficiently relaxed state when we watch television or read a book and, whilst these offer us an escape from our daily routine, both still fully engage the conscious mind, for we have to concentrate on the conversation or the plot in order to cognitively understand what is happening. Others will say that the only time they relax is when they go to sleep and whilst this is, without question, a wonderful state of non-awareness for our conscious mind, it is a time when the sub-conscious becomes totally dominant and once again little communication takes place between the two unless the sleeper has the ability to both remember and interpret his dreams.

To achieve conscious and sub-conscious communication and allow the still small voice of the soul to speak and be heard, we need to attain a relaxed state of awareness that falls between that of waking and sleeping; a place where the brainwaves slow down sufficiently for communication to take place. Table 1.2 illustrates the known types and frequencies of brainwave activity.

Type of brainwave	Hertz (cycles per second)	State of mind
K Complex	33 +	These occur in short bursts and are associated with moments of enlightenment or clarity.
High Beta	23 – 32	Found in those who suffer from hyperactivity and some anxiety states.
Beta	14 – 22	Normal waking state. Conscious mind fully alert and attention turned fully towards the external world.
Alpha	8 – 13	A relaxed state where the conscious mind begins to release some of its control. We daydream or lose ourselves through body therapy, Tai Chi, hypnotherapy, chanting and meditation.
Theta	4 - 7	A state of deep relaxation,

		experienced through shamanic trance, deep levels of hypnotherapy and meditation, moments of high creativity and when we are on the brink of the sleep state.
Delta	1-6	The deep dreamless sleep state, although on rare occasions these waves have been measured by those who are capable of very deep meditation or psychic activities.

Table 1.2

It is during the two relaxed states of alpha and theta that we are able to achieve real communication between the conscious and unconscious mind. In these states, both are still capable of a certain level of activity, whilst neither is dominant and it is within this space that magick becomes possible.

These states can be experienced through meditation, listening to specific types of music, smelling certain aromas, looking at something beautiful, or experiencing deeply relaxing body therapy, all of which are discussed in detail throughout the following chapters.

It is important then that we all enter into one of these two relaxed states on a regular basis, to enable the conscious mind to quieten sufficiently to let the soul speak, yet be active enough to understand its needs and action them in the material world. In this way we remain true to ourselves as illustrated in the words of Anaïs Nin (born Angela Anaïs Juana Antolina Rosa) who became famous for her published journals, which span more than 60 years, beginning when she was 11 years old and ending shortly before her death:

'When one is pretending, the entire body revolts.'

- Anaïs Nin

The Musings of the Mind

Not all disease begins on a soul level, for some people do honour their soul calling. On the other hand, this does not ensure immunity from the musings of the mind, one of the biggest culprits of disease and disorder in the physical body.

There is no doubt that the mind is a wonderful tool and one that for all our scientific and medical research, we still know very little about. What we do know though is that the working of the brain enables us to function as a human being and, as such, carry out millions of complex actions. In many instances, we allow our thoughts to control us rather than ensuring we control our thoughts and, when we find ourselves in a difficult situation, we tend to give in to negative thought patterns, thereby attracting exactly what we say we do not want.

From an extremely early age we are programmed by parents and teachers in a negative way. We are told not to do things, not to touch things and not to think things, rather than being fed positive statements about what we can do or can achieve. It is a known fact in psychology circles that the mind is incapable of processing negative statements and yet, if we actually listen to the language we use, we will find that much of it is negatively charged, thereby pushing the good things in life away from us.

When a teacher says, 'Don't forget your homework', the child's mind fails to register the word 'don't' and therefore processes the sentence as 'forget your homework'. What the child needs to hear is 'remember your homework.' In essence, the statements are the same, yet one is programmed negatively and the other positively. In the same way as an adult, we might say, 'I don't want to be twenty stone anymore,' or 'I don't want to be ill,' rather than, 'I want to be twelve stone,' and 'I want to be healthy'.

Many of us today are familiar with the law of attraction, which states that when we affirm what we want in a positive way, we will attract that specific thing to us, making what we think and ultimately say so important. Due to our overwhelming attraction to the negative, it is little wonder that many of us spend our lives in a state of constant stress, feeling anxious, frightened, worried, guilt-ridden or sad.

These constant damaging thoughts, coupled with the negative emotions they ignite, lead the physical body to produce a flow of stress related hormones, the culmination of which eventually leads to disease.

'If the mind, that rules the body, ever so far forgets itself as to trample on its slave, the slave is never generous enough to forgive the injury, but will rise and smite the oppressor.'

- Henry Wadsworth Longfellow

Doctor Bernie Siegel, a New York physician and author of *Love, Medicine and Miracle* states: 'Cancer and, indeed, nearly all diseases are psychosomatic.'

By this comment he does not mean that nearly all diseases are *in* the mind, but rather that nearly all diseases *begin* in the mind and that by harbouring the negative feelings that inevitably result from a negatively programmed mind, disease can easily manifest in the physical body.

Many studies have been carried out throughout the world on seriously ill patients, especially those with cancer, by respected physicians, psychologists and complementary practitioners. The conclusions they have reached shows that, through the patients' own admissions, their overriding attitude has been one of resentment, reluctance to forgive, self-pity, self-hatred, bitterness, anger, lack of love, victim mentality, guilt or criticism of the Self or others.

In *Love, Medicine and Miracles,* Dr Siegel writes: 'The simple truth is happy people generally don't get sick.'

Dr Edward Bach, the founder of the Bach Flower Remedies®, went one step further and was quoted as saying: 'All disease is a manifestation of underlying negative states of mind.'

This belief led Dr Bach to eventually leave his orthodox medical practice and set about researching the link between certain illnesses and underlying negative personality traits.

After spending some time at a homeopathic hospital in London, he came across the work of Samuel Hahnemann, the man accredited with the discovery of homeopathic medicine, whose work inspired Bach to go in search of plants whose behaviour mirrored various aspects of the human psyche. This finally led Dr Bach to create the Bach Flower Remedies with which we are familiar today.

Table 1.3 outlines the thirty nine remedies, including the well known 'Rescue Remedy'.

If it is your intention to take these remedies please follow the instructions on the bottle. Please be aware that these remedies do contain alcohol. Always first seek the guidance of a health professional before commencing any treatment not medically prescribed.

Remedy	To Counteract
Agrimony	Inner torture behind cheerful facade
Aspen	Constant feelings of apprehension or dread
Beech	Arrogance of self or criticism and

	intolerance of others
Centaury	Weak will or inability to say 'no'
Cerato	Doubting own judgment and seeking approval of others
Cherry Plum	Uncontrolled irrational thoughts
Chestnut Bud	Repeating the same mistakes
Chicory	Over possessiveness and the martyrdom
Clematis	Absent mindedness or dreaminess
Crab Apple	Feelings of uncleanliness or self hatred
Elm	Temporary moments of doubting one's own capability
Gentian	Despondency
Gorse	Despair and hopelessness
Heather	Obsession with own troubles and over talkativeness
Holly	Jealousy, envy, suspicion and hatred
Honeysuckle	Living in the past and shirking adult responsibility
Hornbeam	The 'Monday morning feeling'
Impatiens	Impatience and irritability
Larch	Lack of confidence and expectation of failure.
Mimulus:	Fear of unknown things
Mustard	Deep gloom and depression
Oak	Feelings of having to carry on regardless of own troubles
Olive	Exhaustion and lack of energy
Pine	Guilt, blame and feelings of unworthiness
Red Chestnut	Over concern of others
Rescue Remedy	Shock, trauma, lack of confidence
Rock Rose	Trepidation, panic and alarm
Rock Water	Harsh treatment of self and self denying
Scleranthus	Uncertainty and indecision
Star of Bethlehem	Shock following bad news or an accident
Sweet Chestnut	Dejection
Vervain	Over enthusiasm, stress and being highly strung
Vine	Domineering, inflexible and arrogant behaviour
Walnut	Resistance to change: child birth, menopause, retirement, redundancy, divorce
Water Violet	Pride, superiority, little emotional involvement
White Chestnut	Unwanted thoughts
Wild Oat	Lack of clarity in discovering one's path

Wild Rose	Drifting through life and apathy
Willow	Feelings of resentment or 'poor me'

Table 1.3

Thoughts create feelings in the body and the body then prepares to act upon them. The body has no way of differentiating between what is subjective (imagined danger) and what is objective (real danger). So if we think or imagine a terrible situation often enough, the body will react as though we have actually experienced it. It is through this type of negative self-hypnosis that we can actually invite illness into our awareness simply by fearing it. Our body, in its obedience, accepts whatever messages we feed it and obligingly comes up with the experience that matches it. Likewise, if we take the time to use positive visualization or affirmations then our body will respond in a positive way.

Positive intent is a key factor in the healing process and any treatment that carries the positive intent of both client and therapist (or doctor) brings an added dimension to the healing process, which often results in an outcome that surpasses all conventional expectations and takes us into the realm of what we may deem to be miracles. In this way, whether we choose to accept it or not, we are all capable to some degree, of creating our own reality.

Reprogramming our thoughts, however, can be a difficult task, especially when we attempt it alone and it is sometimes advisable to seek professional help through clinical hypnosis or neuro-linguistic-programming (NLP), both of which can assist in reframing past traumas and enable life to be looked at from a more positive view point.

As we journey through life, we are constantly asked to make decisions. Those decisions often involve whether to leave things the way they are, or whether to make changes. The more serious the impact on our lives, the more the mind will torment us, regardless of the decision we make.

The example below illustrates how the mind reacts to the person who decides to remain in the same old job: *'Well, you'll never get an opportunity like that again! Just think what would have happened if you'd have gone ... where would you be now, what would you be doing? You'd be far away from this mundane existence....'*

When the opposite decision is made, the mind still torments: *'Well, I hope you're going to do the decent thing and feel guilty. How could you leave everyone in the lurch when they depend on you? You've really burnt your bridges now what if this doesn't work out ... you can never go back!'*

When we are faced with life changing decisions there are no easy options. If we decide to keep things the way they are, then we have to accept that our lives, too, will remain the same and we therefore have to make a conscious decision not to bemoan our lot. Alternatively we can decide to make changes, but have to be aware that this too will often cause disruption to both ourselves and others.

So how do we make a decision that we know will be right? The simple answer is that each person has to decide what is right for them; there are no right or wrong decisions. What we do have to be aware of, nonetheless, is that each decision we make is made for one of two reasons:

HOPE or FEAR

We may make a decision out of hope, in the hope that the aspect of life we are changing will be better than what we have now. Conversely, we may also make a decision out of fear, telling ourselves that at least what we have now is alright. 'Better the devil you know', after all, what if the new way of life doesn't work out?

It is probably because the majority of us make our decisions out of fear rather than hope that our lives are often in a state of disarray, if we could perhaps be less guided by fear and less fearful of hope, our lives would be filled with ease rather than being dis-ease ridden.

The Blessings of the Body

The poor body, it bears the brunt of all the above. When disease or disorder manifest in the physical body, it comes as a final attempt to try to make us listen and warn us that things are not right within a certain aspect of our lives, whether it is a cry from the soul or the conflict of the mind.

'*Criticism may not be agreeable, but it is necessary. It fulfils the same function as pain in the human body. It calls attention to an unhealthy state of things.*'

-Winston Churchill

Whatever the underlying reason for illness to manifest, we must remember that illness comes not as the enemy, but as a friend. As such it speaks to us in a language it knows we will understand and therefore takes the form of pain or disorder. The place and form of the disease however does not happen by chance, for it offers us vital clues as to the nature of the underlying problem.

Many well respected authors have written in depth about the importance of 'Body Speak', including Caroline Myss, Louise Hay and Debbie Shapiro, all of whom agree that the body, for all its complexities, attempts to contact us through being literal in its message. Body speak tells it like it is as illustrated in Table 1.4.

Body Part	**Possible disease/disorder**	**Message**
Head	Migraine Headaches Brain tumour Cognitive disorders	I'm being compressed. I'm under a black cloud. I can't think straight He's doing my head in.
Throat/ Neck	Sore throat Tonsillitis Stiff neck Laryngitis Cervical spine restriction	She's a pain in the neck. I can't speak out. I can't express who I truly am. I can't have an opinion
Hips and Thighs	Arthritic hips Leg pain Sciatica Lumbar spine restriction Buttock pain	I can't move forward. I'm stuck. I don't know where I'm going. I have become rigid in outlook.
Heart and Chest	Asthma Bronchitis Pneumonia Breast cancer Heart disorders	I can't breath. I'm suffocating. I'm heartbroken. I can't get things off my chest.
Urinary/ Kidney disorders	Cystitis Kidney stones Bladder infection	I'm pissed off. I am afraid to go with the flow of life. I have hard unshed tears.

Table 1.4

It therefore becomes easy to appreciate that behind every physical disease is an emotion or thought that in some way corresponds with the area of the body in which it manifests and, that an imbalance in any one area, has the ability to affect others.

If we know how to maintain our health, then why are so many of us still experiencing illness and disease? The answer so often lies in the fact that the majority of us are too preoccupied with work, family and relationships to prioritise our own needs. If on the other hand we fail to make time for ourselves, we may eventually have to make time for disease.

Sometimes it is our treatment of the body itself that can begin to affect the way we feel and the way we perceive ourselves to be, thus dis-ease within the physical body can in turn affect the mind and emotions. Our health can be dramatically improved by taking care of the physical body, for this is the only vehicle we have in this incarnation for carrying our soul around.

Relaxation

In order for the body to become relaxed, the application of therapeutic touch is highly recommended. Not only does it ease aches, pains and tight muscles, but also releases sub-conscious thoughts and emotions which are held, according to Professor Candice Pert of the Centre for Molecular and Behavioural Neuroscience at Rutgers University, in every cell in our body.

A massage is, therefore, far more than an aromatic beauty treatment, as it can begin to release years of negatively charged energy and thereby kick-start the healing process on all levels and is discussed in more detail in Chapter 4.

Diet

What we eat and how we eat, as in the word 'diet', is probably something the majority of us associate with losing weight, however for the purpose of this book the word refers to adopting a healthier way of eating, for with the correct nutrition the body has the building blocks to enable it to fight disease. The intake of sufficient pure water is often capable of rectifying many physical symptoms from general aches and pains to headaches and lack of concentration. These subjects are discussed in more detail in Chapter 6.

Exercise

Being active in one way or another is something that is always welcomed by the body and not only makes us physically stronger, but has also been shown to dramatically improve certain types of depressive states. Just like our car needs a run up the motorway to charge the battery, so our body needs some aerobic exercise to raise the heart rate.

Thankfully this doesn't have to mean visiting the gym or the pool but can include any enjoyable exercise, from running to playing squash, or from housework to gardening; even half an hour's walking at least three times per week is an easy way to keep fit.

It has been proven that exercise increases the good HDL cholesterol in the bloodstream, which is said to protect against heart disease. Exercise also protects against osteoporosis by increasing bone density and combats stress by stimulating endorphins - the feel good hormones in the brain. A major benefit of exercise is that it aids in toning the muscles - fat is burned up more easily - thereby preventing obesity. Overall, regular exercise generally improves sleep patterns, health and longevity.

The Importance of Love and Forgiveness in the Healing Process

There are numerous factors to consider when embarking on the self-healing path. However, as we will find out, love and forgiveness can play a vital role in restoring health.

Love

In order to lead a healthy and happy life, love is one of the key ingredients and can literally make the difference between life and death. Love can, of course, come in many forms: a spouse or partner, children, parents, siblings, good friends or a beloved pet.

When we lose someone close to us, whether through death, dementia or divorce, our immune system can become depressed due to the overwhelming feelings of grief and desolation that follow, often leading to illness due to suffering from what we may term a 'broken heart'.

It is important therefore that we also learn to love ourselves, a task that many of us would tend to shy away from as self-love has always inferred that perhaps we are conceited or vain. This however is far from the truth and by having an appreciation for who we are, we are able to take the first step in the healing process.

Self-hatred is destructive and will depress the immune system like nothing else does. When we are attacked from the outside by someone, we have the option of defending ourselves, but when we are attacked from the inside by ourselves then we are literally defenceless. It is a sad fact that most people do not think highly enough of themselves and this is often the root cause of many illnesses.

Just as our car would lose its sparkle if we were never to polish it, so it is with ourselves. If we fail to show ourselves tender loving care and appreciation then we too become tired and dull.

Loving and experiencing love through a hug, a kind word, or watching a feel good film not only makes us feel good, but actually does us good by stimulating the whole immune system.

Forgiveness

The old adage by Alexander Pope 'to err is human, to forgive is Divine' probably sums up the importance of forgiveness and yet it is something which many of us struggle with and this often becomes the root cause of many illnesses.

We have all heard people say, 'I'll never forgive her for what she did,' or perhaps, 'He doesn't deserve to be forgiven,' leading the victim to live with a lifetime's sentence of resentment, ultimately affecting the mind, body and spirit in a negative way.

How then do we go about forgiving someone? A popular misconception is that forgiveness means forgetting and that is not what forgiveness is about. Forgiveness doesn't agree to forgo justice, it doesn't agree to condone the act that had been committed nor does it agree to forget it. Forgiveness allows us to release ourselves from the negative emotions that surround the event.

When we choose to forgive someone, which on some occasions may be ourselves, we are able to not only release the anger, hatred and blame that we harbour within every cell in our body, but for a brief moment that act of forgiveness enables us to connect with divinity.

So how do we know when we have truly forgiven? The simple answer is that when the person or persons concerned can pass through our mind without disturbance, then and only then has forgiveness been achieved.

Belief and Divine Healing

It is a fact that those who intend to become well, those who visualize themselves being well and those who believe they are becoming well have a greater chance of healing than those who think in a negative way.

For some, however, mere self-belief is not enough and, throughout millennia, mankind has turned to the natural world, to magick, to the angelic realms and to the gods for healing, all of which has become intermingled, one with the other, illustrating that little changes within the human psyche as the centuries pass.

Today science has become the modern god of medicine, a path along which the majority of us venture at some point in our lives. It has also become the path that has, over the last seventy years, relegated natural healing, the gods and magick to a distant time where mists swirled and sacrificial screams pierced the night air. The innate power of these ancient healing practices has never really been silenced and is once again resurfacing, calling us to unearth the power of natural remedies, evoke our deities and weave our magick.

'Phytotherapy' (herbal medicine) derives its name from the Greek word 'phyton', meaning 'plant' and is probably the oldest form of medicine in the world with our only knowledge stemming mainly from remains found in caves and shelters of prehistoric man.

It is thought that ancient man learned how to preserve meat by placing it on a bed of herbs, such as wild mint or rosemary, whilst simultaneously noting how certain illnesses were alleviated when these herbs were ingested.

Firmer evidence in the practice of phytotherapy was provided by the Egyptians who thoughtfully left behind many papyri describing their particular brand of herbal medicine. They knew how to make healing ointments and utilised barley, hops, aloe and thyme to arrest bleeding, help heal wounds and reduce fevers. Even decaying teeth were packed with plant resins.

Their use of plants in healing was inextricably linked

with magick and the worship of the gods. When the gods were angry, disorder came to both the world and mankind and had to be healed by means of magickal incantations and aromatic herbal offerings. The gods to whom these offerings were made included Horus, god of general healing; Thoth, god of medicine and magick; Isis, goddess of fertility and Sekhmet who, when angry, unleashed diseases.

In the classical world, the first health deity was born from the love affair between Apollo and Coronis. Just before Coronis was due to give birth however, she deceived Apollo and married the Arcadian, Ischys.

In a rage, Apollo put both Coronis and Ischys to death and, as the bodies of the two lovers burned together on a funeral pyre; Apollo plucked the unborn child from Coronis' womb and immediately carried him to Mount Pelion, where he was placed into the care of the Centaur Chiron.

As the child, whom Apollo named Asclepius, grew, Chiron instructed him in the art of hunting and the science of medicine, leading Asclepius to embark upon a medical career through which he become revered as the Greek god of medicine.

Asclepius was often symbolised as a serpent and his cult had the dual purpose of being both a religion and a therapeutic system. His sanctuaries, known as the *Asclepeia,* were built on what were considered to be 'healthy sites' outside the towns and cities and the priests who were in charge of them had a monopoly on medical knowledge, which was handed down from father to son.

Within the Asclepeia, many special rites were observed by the sick including: taking purification baths, fasting and making sacrifices before being allowed to spend the night in the temple.

The night spent in the temple was known as the 'period of incubation', during which Asclepius would appear to the patient in a dream. The following day the priests of the temple would interpret the dream and advise the patient as to the action or treatment he should take.

In order to give thanks, the patients would either toss a gold coin into the sacred fountain or hang an ex-voto (illustrated glass and metal plaque) on the wall of the temple.

With his miraculous cures, Asclepius' reputation grew beyond repute, especially when he began restoring the dead to life. He achieved this feat with the combined assistance of Athene's gift of the Gorgon's blood and by means of plant knowledge divulged to him by a serpent.

His actions, however, came to the notice of Hades, who complained to Zeus that the dead were being restored to life rather than entering the underworld. Zeus agreed that mortals should follow their destiny and not be saved from the jaws of death by the gods. Zeus therefore accused Asclepius of thwarting the order of the nature and immediately struck him dead with a thunderbolt.

Asclepius however, had five children, two of whom continued his healing work. His son, Telesphorus, became the guardian spirit of convalescence, whilst one of his four daughters, Hygieia, eventually took over from her father as the goddess of health, cleanliness and sanitation.

Initially Hygieia was the guardian of purely physical health, but in later times her domain also extended to that of mental health and general protection against danger. It is from her name that the word 'hygiene' derives and was used as a greeting by the Pythagoreans to whom it meant 'good health'.

Hygieia was often depicted carrying a snake that wound round her body and drank from a cup, which she held in her hand. This symbolism was perhaps a link to the plant knowledge gained from the snake by her father and has since become synonymous with healing.

Hygieia did not, though, have her own cult until she became recognised by the Oracle at Delphi following the Plague of Athens around 430BC.

With today's interest in the Angelic Realms, the Archangel Raphael is often in great demand with regards to health related matters. The name Raphael means 'healing god' (and many variations with the same meaning) and he is considered to be one of seven archangels who stand before the throne of the Christian God. Although not mentioned by name in the standard Christian Bible, he does appear in the Jewish apocryphal book of Enoch, where he first comes to light disguised in human form as 'Azarias, son of the great Ananias'.

In the *Book of Enoch*, Azarias appeared to Tobit, Tobiah and Sarah. He healed Tobit's blindness and drove out demons from Sarah, who was then able to marry Tobiah. Following these healings, Raphael disclosed his true identity.

It has been suggested that Raphael was the angel who helped Abraham heal from his circumcision and who also answered King Solomon's fervent prayers for help in building his temple. Raphael reputedly gave Solomon a ring engraved with a five-pointed star that had the power to subdue all demons and subsequently use them as labourers to complete the building.

Raphael was also considered to be the angelic equivalent of the winged messenger gods, Hermes and Mercury, and, like them, had as his symbol the serpent or caduceus.

He was revered as the guardian angel of medical workers, matchmakers, the blind, travellers and happy meetings and his feast day was, and still is, celebrated on 29 September.

Today he is looked upon as the archangel of healing who bestows healing miracles and blessings upon humankind.

Conclusion

The nature of healing and disease is a vast and complex subject, neither of which can be looked at in isolation.

When a disease manifests, it is natural for us to immediately begin treatment of the symptom, however it also becomes vitally important to begin investigating the reason behind the disease. We must therefore give consideration to the way we feel, our dominant thought processes and our heartfelt desires, peeling away the layers until the cause of unrest is found and then making the life changes necessary to bring about a state of harmony and health.

In the following chapter the subject of healing and disease is explored in terms of energy as we investigate the role of the aura or human energy field.

Mrs Darley Tale: Elf-Shot

Teetering on a rather precarious stepladder, I was just securing the final piece of seasonal greenery above Mrs Darley's granite fireplace when Lucy burst into the cottage.

'Have you ever heard of *elf-shot*?' she asked.

'Well and hello to you too,' Mrs Darley smiled.

Mrs Darley's comment, however, was lost as Lucy only had one thing on her mind.

'How can something be shot at by elves when they

don't even exist?' she said.

At this point, I jumped off the ladder and returned to the safety of the slate floor, intrigued by the unusual topic of conversation that was about to ensue.

'And what has stirred your interest in the existence or otherwise of the elven kingdom?' Mrs Darley asked.

'Rachel Tregowan's granny says her cows are sick because of elf-shot.' Lucy replied.

'Does she now?' said Mrs Darley, 'and what do you make of that?'

Lucy shrugged, 'I don't know. The vet says he doesn't know what's caused it and so Rachel's Granny says it must be "elf-shot". Rachel's dad told her not to be ridiculous because elves don't really exist, apart from in *Lord of the Rings* and things, so why would she say such a thing?'

'Perhaps, because the vet is unable to give her the answers she wants, she turned to the fairy realm for a reason,' said Mrs Darley. 'You see, Lucy, back in Saxon times everyone believed in elves. They were said to be the most beautiful, radiant creatures to which great respect was given. However,' Mrs Darley raised her finger, 'they were also known to cause harm to humans, showering them with sudden pain, such as a stitch or cramp and quite often they were said to cause illness in sheep and cattle. In fact, I remember learning a verse by the poet William Collins way back in my youth.

There every herd, by sad experience, knows
How, winged with fate, their elf-shot arrows fly,
When the sick ewe her summer food forgoes,
Or, stretched on earth, the heart-smit heifers lie.

I watched as Lucy mulled over the words of the poem

before allowing her logical mind to win the internal battle. 'Well I still don't think elves exist,' she said as much to convince herself as anyone else, 'do you?'

Mrs Darley smiled, 'Who is to say, my dear? That is a question that we each must answer for ourselves. Rachel's granny believes they do and you believe they don't. Where then does the answer lie?'

A Plea to Asclepius

From Serpent's words
Come arcane knowledge,
From Gorgons blood
A healing charm.

Bolt the door
Where death stands waiting,
Asclepius!
Save us from harm.

Chapter 2

The Subtle Energy Fields

Energy
Dancing between us
Around us
Within,

We stand not apart,
But each is
Akin,

All woven together
By life's silver
Thread,

Bound to each other,
Our energy
Wed.

Mrs Darley Tale: The Dark Night of the Soul
They say that eavesdroppers never hear anything good about themselves, but I really wasn't eavesdropping, I just happened to overhear something that I wished I hadn't.

It was early spring and upon arriving home from work, I followed my usual routine of going outside to collect a few logs and a bucket of coal from the little bunker beside the porch in order to light my fire.

Finishing my noisy shovelling and turning to pick up my bucket, I could clearly hear the voices of Mrs Darley and Phyllis drifting through the open window.

'So he's asked us to do a healing ritual then?' Phyllis said.

'Yes,' Mrs Darley replied, 'I said we'd arrange it for Saturday as the new crescent will be visible in the evening sky.'

'Are you going to ask our novice neighbour to participate?' Phyllis asked.

I am ashamed to admit that I immediately put down my bucket and crouched alongside the wall, for I knew that they were discussing me.

'No,' said Mrs Darley, 'I don't think so.'

'Why ever not?' Phyllis asked.

'Because I don't think she's ready. Oh, she appears to be fascinated by the subjects we discuss, but she hardly ever pushes for knowledge and to be perfectly honest I think she's afraid.'

'Afraid?'

Mrs Darley continued, 'Yes, afraid of becoming involved in something that she still feels is wrong somehow, despite all of our talks and celebrations. More than that, however, I think she is afraid that she might have to make changes in her life, a subject we've discussed on many an occasion....'

I had heard enough and, feeling both hurt and angry that I was the subject of their judgmental conversation, I made my way back into the cottage and slammed the door, berating myself for even caring what they thought of me anyway.

After cooking a meal and licking my wounds for an hour or so I rang my parents and suggested that I might visit them for the forthcoming weekend, which meant that I would be away on the day of the planned ritual. Mum was delighted and asked if I would accompany her to see her goddaughter's little boy perform at church on Sunday morning in his creation play. I naturally agreed and, in some strange way, the thought of going back to church actually comforted me, for this was a return to my roots and was perhaps, where I really belonged.

Seeing my parents restored my spirits and on Sunday morning, Mum and I went to church to watch Toby's creation play.

Initially I found the atmosphere of the church soothing, but as the vicar stood to deliver the sermon, my feelings began to change and I began to realise why my faith in the church had faltered in the first place. I listened to the outpouring of anger from the Christian God as he advised Adam why we have to suffer death and how Eve's misdemeanour had brought about the downfall of man.

Suddenly I began to feel terribly confused. I knew for certain that there was no way I could return to the teachings of the Christian church, but felt that I didn't belong in Mrs Darley's world either and yet, I had found more peace and solace in her gatherings and the celebrations of the old festivals than I had ever found in any Biblical doctrine. As I drove back down the M5 later that afternoon, I felt spiritually caught between a rock and a hard place.

I had been home an hour or so when there was a knock at the door and I could see Mrs Darley standing in the porch with a tray. Still smarting from the overheard conversation with Phyllis, I decided to be polite but cool.

'Hello, dear,' she said offering me the tray, 'here's a welcome home tea, just a pasty and a few scones with a dish of clotted cream.'

'Thank you,' I said, taking the tray from her. 'That's very kind.'

Mrs Darley smiled and hesitated for a moment, 'Are you alright, dear?'

I nodded, 'Just tired after the drive, that's all.'

She nodded. 'Did you hear about Don?'

I shook my head.

'He's been diagnosed with skin cancer.'

I felt my head reeling for a moment as I took in this rather shocking information. 'Oh, I am sorry. I didn't know. How is he?'

'He's taken it surprisingly well, although I don't doubt he has his moments of dark thoughts,' she said.

'I'm sure he does,' I agreed, 'look if there's anything I can do....' I let the sentence trail away into the air.

'There is actually,' Mrs Darley said. 'Why don't you pop round later after you've enjoyed your meal and we'll have a chat?'

I nodded, my coolness beginning to melt a little, 'I will and thanks for this,' I said lifting the tray to acknowledge her gift.

She smiled. 'You are very welcome, my dear, I'll see you later.'

It was around 8.30 when I finally stood outside Mrs Darley's cottage door with her tea tray and an assortment of plates in my hand.

'Come in,' she called from an upstairs window, 'I won't be a minute.'

I went in and made myself comfortable in my favourite fireside chair and within a few minutes was joined by Mrs Darley and a tot of her favourite whisky.

'Did you have a good weekend?' she asked.

'Yes, yes I did, although it did make me stop and think.'

'In what way?' she asked.

'I went to church this morning.'

'And?'

'And it doesn't rest easy with me anymore.'

'Is that so bad?' she asked.

'I don't know. I was sort of hoping that I would feel as though I had returned home by going back to church.'

'And you didn't?'

I shook my head. 'No, in fact I felt more alienated than ever by the sermon. There's no place in the Christian church where the strength, power and beauty of women are celebrated, only women who are disobedient, subservient or who are in need of saving are mentioned. That's something that up until today I've never really thought about, but this morning it really seemed to rub me up the wrong way and I began to see the church for what it really was, a patriarchal institution that seeks to control man through fear and make women second class citizens .'

'Goodness,' said Mrs Darley, 'that's the first time I've ever heard you speak with real passion about anything.'

'Oh, dear,' I laughed, 'is it really? Perhaps I shouldn't have gone to church this morning after all?'

'Not at all, it was good to hear your views and as for thinking that perhaps you shouldn't have gone back to church, sometimes we have to return to the past in order to let it go, otherwise we can be in danger of allowing our imagination to conjure up a rose tinted haze over something that we should, in reality have left long ago.

'So tell me, my dear, where does your true path lie?'

I don't know,' I said.

'Now that's no answer from someone who spoke with such passion only a few moments ago,' Mrs Darley replied. 'However, I think you are experiencing what is often termed as the "dark night of the soul".'

'Which is?' I asked.

'Which is an inner conflict. You are currently experiencing inner conflict over your spiritual beliefs, making you feel confused about where your true path lies.'

I sighed and looked at her, 'I thought I knew until last week.'

'And what happened last week?' she asked.

'I overheard a conversation,' I said, the colour springing to my cheeks.

'And what conversation would that be?' she said.

'A conversation between you and Phyllis about me and the fact that you didn't feel I was ready to join you.'

'I see,' she said slowly, 'and following that conversation you now presumably think you're not worthy of following this path that the likes of Phyllis and I have embarked upon?'

I shrugged, unsure of what to say.

'My dear,' she said, 'if you had stayed and listened to the whole conversation you would have heard far more complimentary things said about you than what you deemed to be detrimental and, you would no doubt have heard me being severely berated by Phyllis for presuming to know what was right for you without actually asking you personally.'

'Oh,' I said, feeling momentarily at a loss for words.

'However, I still stand by what I said in that I do think you are afraid of this Pagan, or nature based path, call it what you will. In fact I think you find it both fascinating and terrifying in equal measure. Am I correct?'

'I nodded.

'What are you afraid of exactly?'

'I don't want to get involved in witchcraft.' I said.

'And what do you think constitutes witchcraft?' she asked.

'Evil spells, dark forces, manipulation …' I offered.

Mrs Darley laughed. 'Then no wonder you're afraid!'

'Black magick then? Oh, I don't know,' I said, throwing my hands up in the air in a gesture of frustration.

'I cannot deny, my dear, that on some occasions the energy raised during the practise of magick is used to control or manipulate. After all, mankind is easily seduced by the ways of the material world, but if magick is used for the good, then surely it is a wonderful thing?'

'But we're not supposed to live a life full of magick,' I protested. 'Aren't we supposed to experience conflict and pain?'

'I don't know, my dear, are we? Are you sure you're not quoting the teachings of more orthodox religions? After all, what's wrong with using a little bit of magick to attract positive influences into your life?'

'It's manipulative. It interferes with fate.'

'Ah, fate,' said Mrs Darley. 'So if you saw your mother being abused by someone in the street would you do something about it or just leave her to her fate?'

'That's different.'

'How? How is your interference in order to influence a beneficial outcome any different from working with nature's natural forces to achieve the same aim?'

I shook my head. 'I don't know.'

'The use of magick simply aligns us to the ebb and flow of nature. We work, as you should have an appreciation of by now, with the rhythm of the seasons, the moon's phases, the oil yield of plants and with the natural elements that surround us. We state our goals and plan in the spring; at the crescent moon, in the east, at the breaking of the dawn. We bring our goals to fruition in the summer when the sun is the height of his power, at the full moon, in the south and at midday. We reap the benefits of our actions in the autumn, during the waning moon, in the west, in the evening and we rest and retreat in the winter, at the time of the dark moon, at midnight, in the north. We use magick, my dear, to enhance our lives and the lives of those who ask, we do not use it in order to manipulate the lives of others, which,' she continued, 'is where Don comes into the equation.'

'In what way?' I asked.

'Don asked us to perform a healing ritual for him and although we did that last night, there are many more opportunities for working in synch with nature as the month progresses.

'On Tuesday the moon enters the sign of Capricorn, which governs the health of the skin and, if you would like to help to send healing energy to Don then you might like to try a simple ritual at home.'

'I nodded. 'Yes I would.'

Mrs Darley reached into the cupboard beside her chair and handed me a blue candle. 'Simply carve the word 'healing' and Don's name into this candle, light it and concentrate on your goal, which is to see Don healthy and well. When you feel as though you have done this for long enough, simply thank the energies and allow the candle to burn down of its own accord.'

'But how can the fact that I am just thinking about Don actually help him?' I asked.

'Because thoughts are energy and energy, as we've discussed before, is all there is, therefore your thoughts can affect anything you choose to focus on, just like a prayer. You see, for all its brilliance, the mind is unable to differentiate between what is real and what is imagined, therefore visualizations can be as powerful as actions.'

'Can I ask you a question?' I asked.

Mrs Darley nodded.

'Are you a witch?'

'I dislike labels.'

'But if you had to have a label, would you call yourself a witch?' I persisted.

'Some would say so, yes.'

'I see,' I said.

'Oh, my dear,' she said, 'you haven't even begun to.'

Understanding Energy

Everything is connected. Nothing stands apart. This concept was proved by Einstein through his formula of $E = mc^2$, which illustrates that matter and energy are simply different forms of the same thing; matter can be turned into energy and energy into matter.

Therefore, if everything is energy, there is no separation between anything that is, for it all forms part of the whole. If we chose to damage or neglect ourselves, we damage and neglect the whole, likewise if we love and care for ourselves then love and caring will be bestowed upon the whole. In the words of Mahatma Gandhi: 'Be the change you want to see.'

The majority of us intuitively grasp the connection between energy and good health and are familiar with the terms 'lacking in energy' or 'feeling drained of energy' as phrases we would use to describe ourselves at times when we feel under par.

Thinking in terms of the amount of energy we have is central to the holistic view of our general health. Virtually all complementary therapies are based upon viewing life as an energy process. Each therapy, regardless of its type, attempts to correct energy imbalances in a variety of ways, whether this is via touch, smell, taste, sight or sound. But what exactly is this energy to which we refer so casually and how can it affect everything in the Universe?

Modern physics tells us that the only difference between various forms of energy is that each vibrates at a different frequency, with solid objects vibrating at a much slower rate than those which appear invisible to the naked eye, such as electricity. In addition to this, the space between one object and another is also filled with energy, a phenomenon generally referred to as 'The Universal Energy Field'.

This is not, however, a new phenomenon, for ancient Indian traditions, some 5,000 years old, referred to the existence of universal energy called *Prana,* which was seen as being the source of all life. The Chinese also recognised a similar phenomenon called *Chi,* which they considered to have two opposing forces called *Yin* (feminine) and *Yang* (masculine).

The universal energy field is unique in so much as it appears to defy the second law of thermodynamics, which states that it is impossible to get more energy out of something than is put in. However, no matter how much energy we take from the universal energy field it continues to remain constant.

Each human being is also surrounded by a specific field of energy, often referred to as 'The Human Energy Field' or 'Aura'. This field is simply a manifestation of the universal energy field that is intimately involved with human life.

For millennia, mystics and followers of many religious paths have spoken about being able to perceive a halo of light around people's bodies. The first recorded literary evidence for this phenomenon dates back to 500BC, when Pythagoreans stated that this energy or light, according to its quality, could produce a variety of effects in the human organism, including the cure of disease.

The early twelfth century scholars Boirac and Liebeault noted that the human energy field was capable of interacting at a distance and went on to record that one person is able to have a beneficial or detrimental affect on another, simply by his or her presence. Paracelsus went on to call this phenomenon *Iliaster (*or *Yliaster*), referring to something that is both a vital force and is composed of vital matter.

In the nineteenth century, the mathematician, Helmont, and the instigator of the hypnotic state, Mesmer, confirmed the findings of their predecessors, whilst also taking matters one step further by reporting that both animate and inanimate objects were charged with this 'vital fluid', which could indeed exert an influence on others at a distance. They considered that the behaviour of this fluid suggested the existence of some kind of electromagnetic field.

During the mid 1800s, Count Wilhelm von Reichenbach spent thirty years of his life experimenting with this field, which he called the *odic force* and found that it had several rather odd properties. One of these was, that unlike in electromagnetism, where opposite poles attract, the odic field produced poles, where like poles attracted like, a polarity phenomenon also exhibited in crystals. Therefore, what we put out in energy terms we also attract.

In 1911, Dr William Kilner, a medical doctor, observed the human energy field through coloured screens and coined the term 'aura'. He discovered through his studies that the aura differed greatly according to age, sex, mental ability and health and that certain illness showed up as patches or tears, which led him to develop a diagnostic system based on the colour, texture, volume and general appearance of this luminous energy body.

In the intervening years, many eminent doctors and scientists have studied both the universal and human energy fields and attempted to measure them on increasingly more advanced pieces of equipment.

In the mid 1900s, Dr Wilhelm Reich constructed a variety of appliances one of which was the *accumulator* that was capable of concentrating universal energy, which he then used to charge other objects. Other pieces of scientific equipment have included the Japanese *biological detector* made from a leaf vein that was connected to a photo quantum device, which measured the quantity of energy that radiated out from the human body.

In the early 1940s, a Russian electrician and amateur inventor, Seymon Kirlian, captured an image of his hand whilst using a process which involved photographing subjects in the presence of a high-frequency, high-voltage, low-amperage, electrical field. The resulting image clearly showed an unusual orange glow emanating from his fingertips and Kirlian began to realise that he had perhaps found a way of visually capturing evidence of the human bio field or energy field.

From this point, Seymon and his wife Valentina, a biologist, began to photograph both animate and inanimate objects using the same technique and became convinced that there was a definite link between the strength and visual impact of the human aura and health. However, despite much work carried out by American scientists in the 1970s on this particular photographic method, the technique still has both its champions and its critics.

There have been numerous studies carried out during the past 100 years, which have studied both the human aura and chakra system in-depth, proving beyond doubt that they are far more than a New Age fantasy, or a phenomenon that should be confined to the myths of the past. The human energy field or aura does indeed reflect an individual's health, on a physical, emotional, psychological and even spiritual basis.

Exploring the Human Energy Field (Aura)

Based on their own observations, many experts in the topic of the human energy field have created their own systems in order to define the auric field, which have included: location, brightness, density, fluidity, form and colour. The human energy field, in general terms, can be described as: a luminous body that surrounds and interpenetrates the physical body.

The aura consists of several layers, generally accepted to be seven, although this does vary according to opinion. The eminent healer and scientist Barbara Ann Brenan is of the opinion that the human aura comprises of what she describes as a 'dualistic field pattern'. That is, that every other layer of the aura is highly structured like standing waves of light patterns (layers 1, 3, 5, 7), whilst the layers in between (2, 4, 6) appear to look like coloured fluids in motion.

Perhaps the term 'layer' is a slightly misleading one, for this often conjures up an incorrect image of the human energy field being rather like an auric onion, whereas in reality each succeeding layer interpenetrates all the other layers beneath, including the physical body and not only occupies the same space, but slightly exceeds it. Each layer has a particular function and each is composed of finer substances and vibrates at a higher frequency than the body before it.

The human energy field has several roles, each of which is vital, in its own way, to our overall health and well-being.

Predicts

Coming into contact with another person's auric field provides us with the ability to predict how we might feel about someone we meet, some people make us feel instantly at ease, whilst others make us feel decidedly uncomfortable. This is an idea suggested by early twelfth century scientists Boirac and Leibeault, who thought that the energy of others could be either beneficial or detrimental to our health. Therefore our initial reaction to someone's energy or vibe is probably the correct one, as it goes way beyond the critical conscious assessment of the mind, which often persuades us to ignore our gut instinct; a decision we very often come to regret.

Protects

The aura, if strong and vibrant, can protect us from disease on many levels, for it is capable of protecting us from the negative vibrations of others who may wish to drain us of our energy in order to bolster their own. We have all used the expression, 'I feel drained after spending half an hour with her / him,' and people who affect us in this way are often referred to as 'energy vampires'.

If, however, our energy field is strong then we are able to escape unharmed from those who seek to thrive on our energy.

Responds

The aura responds to our physical, emotional, psychological and spiritual state, adapting its shape, colour, vibrancy, fluidity and form according to what is happening in life at any given time.

Records

The human energy field acts as a history book and records our physical health, our emotional state, our thoughts and our connection to a Divine essence.

The field is capable of falling into disrepair when there are negative issues in life that have been left unresolved. In contrast, the aura is capable of becoming strengthened when we experience love, laughter and happiness.

Each layer of the aura is unique and although opinions differ in both the role and number of layers. Table 1.5 illustrates the classic seven layers.

Auric Layer	Role
The First Layer or the Etheric body	The etheric body penetrates the physical body and extends outward by a half to two inches. It pulsates at around fifteen to twenty cycles per minute and is blue to light grey in colour. It derives its name from the word 'ether', meaning 'the state between energy and matter' and contains the blueprint for the physical body. Before birth it helps to guide foetal cellular growth and during life it mirrors human health. A blueprint of disease is thought to manifest in this layer before it becomes noticeable in the physical body.
The Second layer or the Emotional body	The emotional body penetrates both the physical and etheric body and extends beyond the physical body by one to three inches. Its structure is far more fluid than the etheric body and is often seen as fine rainbow coloured clouds. These clouds of colour vary according to the emotional health of the individual. When there is emotional trauma, colours often appear dull and muddy, whilst in happier times the colours

	are bright and vibrant. This layer acts as a bridge between the physical body and the mind.
The Third layer or the Mental body	The mental body penetrates all those previously mentioned and extends outward from the physical body by three to eight inches. This fine layer is associated with the quality and clarity of thought and usually appears as a bright yellow light particularly around the head and shoulders as ideas are formed as blobs of energy. Often these thought blobs are gilded with colours from the emotional layer, which depict the emotions associated with the thoughts emitted.
The Fourth layer or Astral body	The astral layer penetrates all the layers previously mentioned and extends out beyond the physical body by some twelve to eighteen inches. This layer comprises of beautiful clouds of colour which are finer than those of the emotional layer with a rose tinted hue. This is the layer which links the lower earthly energies to the higher vibrations of the spiritual realms. It is the layer through which we love and experience feelings of attraction. When two people are attracted to each other, but have not physically communicated, an energy exchange on the astral level will already have taken place to ascertain whether they are compatible.
The Fifth layer or 'Etheric template body' (according to Barbara Ann Brennan)	This layer penetrates all those below it and extends out from the physical body by eighteen to twenty four inches. It is blue in colour and carries the spiritual blueprint of the etheric level (first level), which in turn, carries the blueprint for the physical body. Therefore when disease manifests in the physical body or the etheric field, the etheric template body lends support to the etheric layer in order that it might be returned to its original healthy blueprint thereby bringing healing to the physical body.
The sixth layer or the Celestial body	This layer penetrates all those below it and extends out from the physical body by twenty four to thirty three inches. It comprises of beautiful shimmering pastel coloured light. This is the emotional level of the spiritual plane and is the layer through which we are able to experience spiritual ecstasy. This layer becomes more defined when we reach the point of realising our connection to the universe and feel that we have a meaningful relationship with a Divine essence.

The seventh layer, the Ketheric template or Causal body	This layer penetrates all those below it and extends out from the physical body by some thirty to forty two inches. It vibrates at an extremely high frequency and appears as a golden, silver light that seems to contain the rest of the auric field within a protective egg shape. This layer is the mental level of the spiritual plane and develops as we become aware that we are one with a Divine essence. This level also contains the main power current that runs up and down the spine and which is responsible for nourishing the whole body. In addition it is also thought to house strands of past lives.

Table 1.5

Once we have an understanding of the human aura it becomes easy to appreciate its importance in our overall health. The more intact, vibrant and fluid the aura is, the healthier we remain.

As our immune system becomes enhanced through laughter, making love, eating nutritious food and a myriad of other activities that bring us joy, so the human energy field also becomes strengthened in the same way.

It is a sad fact, though, that life often calls for us to become involved in more mundane or unpleasant tasks, such as looking after a loved one who is ill, housework or finances, all of which take us away from pursuits that enhance our energy field. It therefore becomes necessary to have a system in place that will energise the auric field whilst we are otherwise engaged.

This system comes in the form of a highly efficient vertical flow of energy that runs up and down the energy field channel, alongside the spinal column. This column of energy extends out beyond the physical body, above the head and below the coccyx.

Where there is a power current, it is usual to have something which actually makes a connection between the appliance (the energy field) and the power current itself, which in this case are spinning cones of energy known as *chakras*.

Exploring the Chakras

Just as there are seven layers to the human energy field, so there are seven major chakras, one for energizing each layer.

The chakras (the word being derived from the Sanskrit meaning 'wheel') are shaped like spinning ice-cream cornets and within each one are smaller spinning vortices. These vortices vary in number according to each energy centre; increasing as the frequency increases.

The tips of the chakra cone plug neatly into the power current column, whilst the open end of the cone extends out as far as the layer of the aura to which it is linked.

In general terms the chakras have three specific functions:

1. To energize the auric field.
2. To monitor the state of the individual's spiritual, mental, emotional and physical health.
3. To gradually help us to develop different states of awareness as we journey through life.

The chakras and their specific connections to our mind, body and spirit can, in a large percentage of cases, provide us with a subtle messaging system in much the same way as 'body speak' was seen to do in the previous chapter. They can, if we are prepared to listen, let us know how we may be consciously or unconsciously blocking a certain aspect of our true selves.

This understanding on the energetic level of our being is able to provide us with the key to healing, as opposed to settling for a mere cure or postponement of physical symptoms. The chakras are, in fact, a better monitor of health than the aura itself, with disease often showing in the chakras before it manifests in the human energy field or the physical body.

Chakra 1

Name and colour	**Connected layer of the aura**	**Position on physical body**	**Physical organs, body systems and sense**
Base, Root or Tribal Red	First or Etheric.	Base of spine facing down towards the earth.	Anus, Rectum, Coccyx, Legs, Feet, Spine, Adrenal glands. Excretory, skeletal and immune systems. Sense of touch.

The base chakra is the first to develop at birth and it is this energy that connects us to the earth plane. Understandably this chakra is concerned with matters connected to security and belonging. It thrives on social order and helps us to absorb group thoughts and become involved in the activities of significant others during our formative years.

It is also the chakra that becomes activated when we join associations or organisations during our lifetime and it is this centre of belonging that is stirred when a family member does something to be proud of, or when we listen to the national anthem.

As we grow into adulthood the base chakra becomes disturbed when there are threats about survival or the ability to provide for our own family.

Problems often occur when thought patterns that were once acceptable as a child are still rigidly followed as an adult, even though we may feel that we have outgrown them. For example, as an adult, we may no longer wish to practice the religion into which we were indoctrinated as a child, yet we find ourselves feeling guilty about not adhering to what was once a tribal activity.

What we must learn to do is to free ourselves from things which no longer form part of who we are as an adult. If we fail to do so and allow these feelings of guilt or unease to fester, then both the base chakra and the etheric layer of the aura can become damaged and ultimately manifest as disease and disorder in the physical areas of the body governed by this energy centre.

Anna's Story

During my time in Cornwall, in order for us to continue practicing as financial advisors, new rules and regulations governing the financial services industry deemed that we should all have a certain qualification by a specific date.

Anna, a colleague of mine, had failed the exams twice and the external examination body stipulated that they could only be taken a maximum of three times. The pressure on Anna was immense, for she knew her job was on the line if she failed for the third time.

It was, therefore, little surprise that she began to manifest physical symptoms, which in her case was sciatica, meaning that her exam date had to be delayed due to the fact that she was unable to sit in any one position for an extended period of time.

No doubt this enforced period of rest was just what she needed, as Anna did eventually pass her exams and had little trouble with sciatica afterwards, except in times of stress.

Chakra 2

Name and colour	Connected layer of the aura	Position on physical body	Physical organs, body systems and sense
Sacral Orange	Second or Emotional.	Between the pubic bone and the navel.	Bladder, Large intestine, Lumbar spine, Pelvis, Appendix, Hips, Sexual organs, Gonads, Excretory and Reproductive systems.

The sacral chakra develops around the age of two to three, when we begin to form relationships outside of the home and, as such, begin to create our own reality. This chakra is involved with creativity, the forming of relationships and the associated challenges of each, including; lack of self-expression, blame, guilt, ethics, money, sex, power, control and fear.

Problems occur in this chakra when we either deny our creative side, or become involved in destructive or damaging relationships whether at work, within our families or in a sexual context.

Tricia's Story

Whilst working as a complementary therapist at a well known golfing hotel, Tricia came along for an aromatherapy massage and, during the case study, confided that she found her husband physically repulsive and that she only stayed with him because of the lifestyle he was able to provide.

As the case history continued, I discovered that she had just completed a course of chemotherapy for cervical cancer.

She became extremely upset as she described her

treatment and the harrowing side effects it had had on her physical and psychological health. She opened up as to the dark places she had found herself in following diagnosis.

I explained the negative impact that living with someone who repulsed her was having on her physical body. She said that although she could appreciate what I was saying, she felt that she was now hopefully cured and was not willing to give up the lifestyle that her husband's wealth afforded her.

I never saw her again, but often wonder whether she ever fully regained her health, as she was a classic example of someone who suffered from the 'golden handcuff syndrome', where a person remains with their partner simply for the material benefits the relationship brings.

Chakra 3

Name and colour	**Connected layer of the aura**	**Position on physical body**	**Physical organs, body systems and sense**
Solar Plexus Yellow	Third or Mental layer.	Directly under the sternum.	Stomach, Liver, Gall bladder, Spleen, Small intestine, Mid spine, Kidney Pancreas. Nervous and Digestive systems

The solar plexus chakra develops around the age of seven when we begin to be aware of who we are. It is often referred to as our 'personal power centre', as it is connected to how we see ourselves and how we think we are perceived by others, therefore having implications on our self-esteem, self-respect, quality of self-care and self-confidence.

Many people experience blockages in this energy centre and, as a result, spend much of their lives feeling inadequate, as though they will never be as good, as rich, as capable, as witty, as intelligent, as charming, or as pretty as others.

This often results in lack of self-esteem and self-respect, which can manifest as physical problems in the areas mentioned above, especially with regards to nervous disorders due to worrying about how we portray ourselves to the outside world.

Tina's Story

I once worked with Tina, who had been brought up in an abusive environment where she was made to feel totally worthless by her mother. She married at sixteen, had three children in close succession and was a single parent by the age of thirty.

Many of her subsequent relationships were with men who treated her in the same abusive way. When asked why she always chose the same type of man, she said that she didn't deserve anyone nice as she always made everyone's life a misery.

Eventually, after months of feeling unwell and consuming enormous amounts of cakes, biscuits and fizzy pop, she collapsed and was diagnosed with type 2 diabetes.

I believe this disease manifested itself simply because she had no sweetness in her life and refused to either honour or respect her Self.

Chakra 4

Name and colour	Connected layer of the aura	Position on physical body	Physical organs, body systems and sense
Heart	Fourth or	In centre of chest	Heart, Lungs, Breast,

Green	Astral.	in line with the heart.	Ribs Shoulders, Arms, Thoracic spine, Hands. Thymus gland Circulatory and Respiratory systems.

The heart chakra begins to develop around the age of fourteen when the emotional roller coaster of life usually picks up speed. Heart energy is associated with all the feelings that are capable of either taking us into the realms of ecstasy, or plummeting us into the depths of torment and despair. These include; love, hatred, resentment, bitterness, loneliness, grief, commitment, forgiveness, compassion, hope and trust.

The heart centre often suffers from blockages simply because, as human beings, we will, at some point, experience one or more of the emotions listed above. Any positive emotions will be beneficial to our immune system and subtle energy fields, whilst those which cause us long term anguish and despair can eventually manifest in disease and disorder.

Olly and Liz's Story

As a child, I learned the art of ballroom dancing and used to attend regular dances with my parents. On Wednesday evenings we would go to a dance run by a couple called Olly and Liz. As a child I used to find them fascinating, for Olly was a gentle soul, ever patient, ever smiling, even when Liz put a foot wrong. Liz, on the other hand, was a fiery lady, blunt, loud and permanently on a short fuse. By her own admission, however, she always maintained that Olly was her rock and without him she would be nothing.

Shortly after their golden wedding, Liz walked into the

lounge one evening to find Olly having a heart attack. Immediately she ran to his side and as she knelt down beside him she too had a heart attack and sadly died, whilst, ironically, Olly survived. For her, the thought of being alone without the man she loved was too heart breaking to contemplate.

Chakra 5

Name and Colour	**Connected layer of the aura**	**Position on physical body**	**Physical organs, body systems and sense**
Throat Blue	Fifth or Etheric template.	In the centre of the throat.	Vocal apparatus, Throat, Neck, Cervical spine, Mouth. Thyroid, Parathyroid and Hypothalamus Glands. Respiratory system. Sense of taste.

The throat chakra develops as we reach adulthood and begin to take responsibility for our own lives. As such, it is associated with the expression of will, the pursuance of dreams and the ability to turn them into reality. It has an impact upon our decision making abilities, our judgment and criticism of the self and others and our tendencies towards addictions. It has implications around having faith in the process of life and the ability to acquire knowledge.

The throat centre can become blocked due to the inability to take responsibility for our own lives, preferring the safety of childhood to the exposure of adulthood. Related illnesses can be experienced if we fail to develop through the quest for knowledge, both internal and external, if we deny the power of our dreams and if we fail to express who we truly are.

For many, blockages in this chakra form when a negative outlook becomes dominant and criticism and judgement becomes second nature, rather than accepting that no one, including ourselves, is perfect and that each person should be accepted for who they are rather than constantly sitting in judgement.

Kelly's Story

Kelly's father had firm ideas about his daughter's career path and, imposing his will upon her, decreed that she would take a degree in science. She struggled with the course, but managed to scrape a degree and, not having any real interest in the subject, applied for a job as a lab technician, which her father considered to be far below her.

Kelly came to see me because for the fifth time in three years she had just emerged from a broken relationship and wondered where she was going wrong.

It seemed that Kelly chose the same type of man every time; usually someone who was down on their luck or had seemingly lost their direction in life. Due to the fact that Kelly had never exerted her own will over that of her father, subconsciously she would purposely choose this particular type of man as someone upon whom she could easily impose her will. Kelly would help her chosen man out of the mire and then expect him to enter into a loving relationship with her. Unfortunately for Kelly, as soon as the man in question found his feet, he disappeared, leaving Kelly to make the same mistakes over and over again.

During her initial case study, I discovered that her passion was ancient Egypt and her big regret was that she hadn't stood up to her dad and studied Egyptology at university rather than science.

I asked her what was stopping her returning to university at the age of twenty seven and taking the subject she had always dreamed of.

She said that as she still lived with her parents she felt that her dad wouldn't support her in this dramatic change of career and so she had made the decision to leave things as they were.

My husband, a clinical hypnotherapist, gave me a poem by Portia Nelson, entitled 'There's a Hole in my Sidewalk: The Romance of Self-Discovery', to let Kelly read and then to ask her where she saw herself.

This thought provoking poem describes a pavement with a hole in it, into which, the pedestrian falls three times before realising that the same mistakes keep being made. Eventually the pedestrian walks around the hole before finally walking down a different street.

Kelly admitted that she hadn't really moved on from repeatedly falling in the same hole and that she could now see where many of her problems originated.

A few weeks later I arrived at the clinic to find her already waiting on the doorstep. She advised me that the previous month had been very upsetting as her father had been diagnosed with terminal stomach cancer, but that he had apologised to her for trying to constantly dominate her life.

She considered this an opportunity too good to miss and went on to tell him of her dream of studying Egyptology and he gave her his blessing.

The outcome for Kelly was bitter sweet; for her dad died just four weeks later, whilst she went on to obtain her doctorate in a subject which meant everything to her.

Kelly now enjoys healthy relationships with the opposite sex, without the need to choose men whom she can easily manipulate.

Chakra 6

Name and colour	**Connected layer of the aura**	**Position on physical body**	**Physical organs, body systems and sense**
Brow, Forehead or Third eye or Tribal. Red	Sixth or Celestial.	In the centre of the forehead just above the bridge of the nose.	Lower brain, Left Eye, Ears, Nose. Pituitary and Pineal Gland. Nervous system. Sense of Sight, Hearing and Smell.

The brow chakra does not normally develop until adulthood and sometimes remains underdeveloped throughout life.

Many people are intelligent, but fail to have emotional intelligence or an understanding of either their own feelings or the feelings of others. This includes the ability to stop what we are doing in life, to learn from life's experiences and, to regularly self-evaluate, in order to determine whether we are on the right path.

Brow energy wants us to be open to the ideas of others, whilst encouraging us to search for our own personal truth and to accept ourselves for who we are.

It is also known as the 'third eye centre', which is the chakra through which we are able to intuit certain pieces of information that cannot be known through our physical senses alone

This chakra fails to develop properly if we simply live life on the basic physical, emotional and psychological levels, thereby denying who we really are at the level of the soul and failing to engage with the higher realms of existence.

Dorothy's Story

A lady in her mid sixties came to see me to enquire as to whether reiki would be able to help with her diagnosis of glaucoma. During the case study, she disclosed that her whole life had been, and still was, spent looking after others, often to the detriment of her own wants and needs and she now felt that she had left it too late to do anything.

We talked about glaucoma being a build up of pressure in the eye, which could, if left untreated, result in a severe deterioration of sight or blindness. We also explored the symbolic meaning of glaucoma and discussed the fact that it sometimes represented not liking what we see in our lives or a fear of looking ahead into a future.

I suggested that she should advise those members of her family who took her time for granted, that at the age of sixty-six she felt she needed to slow down a little and to make time for herself.

She agreed to make a list of all the things she would love to do with her time and then set time aside each day or each week to embark upon at least one thing on her list.

Dorothy came to see me on several occasions during the following six months and informed me that her family had been more than supportive of her new interests. She had begun classes in both life drawing and tai chi and her subsequent visit to the eye specialist revealed that the pressure in her eye had stabilized.

Chakra 7

Name and colour	**Connected layer of the aura**	**Position on physical body**	**Physical organs, body systems and sense**
Crown or	Seventh or	On the crown of	Upper brain, Right

Violet	Ketheric.	head with open cone pointing towards the heavens.	eye, Pineal gland. Muscular system and Skin.

As with the brow chakra, the crown chakra may or may not fully develop and is dependant upon several factors. The first includes the ability to trust life and to accept that it ebbs and flows in cycles, whilst elements of humanitarianism, selflessness and courage also come into the equation. This high vibrational energy encourages us to see the larger picture and helps us to appreciate that we are all unique and have our own particular part to play in the web of life.

The crown centre develops when we begin to have a real and personal relationship with a Divine essence, regardless of whether it is through an orthodox religion, a group based spiritual belief, or via a path of our own choosing.

Ken's Story

A science teacher came along on my aromatherapy course, as he found teaching too stressful and wanted a complete change of career. Initially he loved the course, revelling in the chemistry of the essential oils, the history of aromatic substances and the effect of smell on the brain.

Six months into the course, I announced that the subject matter for the following few weeks would be the impact that essential oils have upon the subtle energy fields and said that this was an aspect of the oils I would expect them all to take into consideration when going through a client's case study.

Immediately I saw his body language change as he folded his arms, which told me in symbolic terms that his mind was closed. He refused to participate in any discussions concerning the auric field, saying that it was new age mumbo jumbo, made up by someone with an overactive imagination, regardless of the fact that he was given a scientific explanation. He went on to make it very clear that this had nothing to do with an aromatherapy massage and that this would be one aspect of the course he would not be participating in.

Over the months that followed the standard of his work fell and he began to complain about muscle pain around his ribs, using this as an excuse for not beginning his case studies. He was eventually diagnosed with fibromyalgia, which ironically is a disease for which there is little explanation.

Ken eventually dropped out of the course, despite much persuasion on my part to encourage him to stay, saying that he had made a mistake and aromatherapy was only for women.

Conclusion

It becomes easy to understand how blockages within the chakra system can lead to rips, tears and a build up of stagnant energy in the corresponding layer of the aura. In turn, physical, emotional, psychological and even spiritual crises can manifest if the flow of energy is not corrected.

In order to instigate this correction, we must look to various types of 'vibrational medicine', which will encourage the subtle energy bodies to vibrate at their optimum level.

Vibrational medicine refers to therapies which have the power to beneficially affect us on more than one level. As discussed, each layer of the aura and each chakra vibrate at different frequencies, therefore by using something with which a particular chakra resonates, we are able to restore harmony to that area, thereby kick-starting the healing process.

The remainder of the book discusses how vibrational medicine works its magick on a mind, body and spirit level and how the five senses of hearing, taste, smell, touch and sight offer endless opportunities to bring harmony to all parts of our being and ultimately help us to begin the healing journey.

Mrs Darley Tale: Making Changes

'Another cold, dear?'

Mrs Darley called to me from her half stable door as I made my way home from work one late August evening.

'You obviously heard me sneezing?' I smiled juggling my laptop, handbag and an assortment of tissues.

'That's the second or third you've had in a matter of months.'

'I know, I just can't seem to build up my immune system and I'm taking extra vitamin C too.'

'Mmmm, perhaps you need a little more than vitamin C,' she said. 'Look, I know it's getting on for nine o'clock, but I haven't eaten yet as Phyllis hasn't long gone, why don't you join me for a pasta supper?'

'But what about this cold? I don't want you to get it.'

'I won't,' she said, 'I'll see you in twenty minutes.'

Without any further encouragement I went home, changed and was back at Mrs Darley's just in time to take charge of a glass of red wine.

'This is a lovely treat,' I said as I stood at the kitchen door watching her put the final touches to what looked like pasta and chicken.

'And one you deserve, my dear,' she said smiling, 'come, let's go through before this gets cold.'

'So why do you think I keep getting these colds?' I asked as we began our meal.

'Because you don't honour who you really are,' she answered. 'In the words of the bard, my dear, *"To thine own self be true, and it must follow, as the night follows the day, thou canst not then be false to any man".'*

'I don't understand what you mean?'

'At the risk of repeating myself, because I've said the same thing to you many times in many ways. You try to be all things to all people and yet I'm not sure you really enjoy any of it.

'Oh, I know you'll protest, after all you're successful at your job, but deep down, at the level of your soul, is it really what you want to do?'

I laughed. 'I don't think I've ever delved into the depths of my soul.'

'And that, my dear, is, where your problem lies,' she said, refilling our glasses. 'At the risk of throwing yet another quote at you, Walt Whitman said, *"Re-examine what you have been taught; discard what wounds your soul".'*

I fell silent and toyed with my food, for only that morning as I sat in a particularly futile sales meeting; I began to wonder what I was doing with my life, which had become an endless round of targets, sales, interviews and small talk.

I thought back to my teenage dreams of becoming a social worker, a teacher of the blind or a problem page writer and wondered when that half caring person had become swallowed up by the commercial world.

'I think you can read my mind sometimes,' I smiled.

She shook her head. 'No, my dear, but I can read your energy levels and yours are certainly not at their peak. So what has your mind been talking to you about?'

'Oh, doing something different. Doing something where I can help people I suppose.'

'And you don't feel as though you do that now?' asked Mrs Darley in a way that was more than just a question.

I shook my head. 'Not in the way I would like. Oh, I know I give financial advice and help people in that way, but I don't really get to make a difference and that's what I feel deep down I should be doing.'

'And how do you see yourself doing that?' she asked gently.

'I don't know exactly, I'd just like to help people feel better about themselves.'

'Some form of healing perhaps?' Mrs Darley suggested.

'Perhaps,' I said.

'Well, those who dip their toe into the waters of the mystical realms are often called to the healing pool, although you must remember that before you can heal others you must first begin the process of healing yourself.'

'Well that's a mammoth task in its own right,' I laughed, 'anyway, I really don't know enough about that sort of thing to make an informed decision and heaven knows when I'd have the time to train.'

'But now you've voiced your intent to the universe, the energy around you will change and you will draw the necessary opportunities and knowledge into your orbit,' said Mrs Darley.

'You make it sound so easy,' I sighed, 'If only changing my life was a matter of just changing my energy.'

'Oh, but it is, my dear,' Mrs Darley replied, 'once your energy changes, everything changes.'

Energy Reading

No one sees,
Yet I feel.

No one tells,
Yet I know.

No one says,
Yet I sense.

Chapter 3

The Senses

Senses
The smell of your skin,
The taste of your mouth,
The sound of your voice,
The sight of your face,
The touch of your hand,

Through my senses I come to know you.

Mrs Darley Tale: Tamarind
It was a hot July morning and there was an excited buzz about the hamlet, for this was the day our new neighbour was moving in.

'I wonder what she'll be like?' Rose asked as she joined Mrs Darley and me for coffee on the pocket of grass just outside the cottages.

'Well, according to Don she's very nice and I don't doubt that he vetted her thoroughly before letting his cottage to her.'

'So how long will Don be away for?' I asked.

'Well his daughter wanted him to move closer to her since his diagnosis, but he really doesn't want to move permanently, so initially he's agreed to stay with her for six months and let out the cottage.'

'Oooo,' said Rose, 'I think I've just heard a van pull up, this could be her now.'

A few moments later there was the bang of van doors and the unmistakable squeak of the gate as someone made their way round the path.

'Good morning, dear,' said Mrs Darley as an attractive raven haired young woman came into view.

'Oh, good morning, isn't this just stunning?' she said making a sweeping gesture with her hands at the view which lay before us.

'It certainly is,' said Mrs Darley, 'and is it a view with which you intend to become familiar?'

'Oh, yes, how rude of me,' the lady laughed, 'I'm going to be renting Don's cottage for six months, I'm Tamarind, how lovely to meet you all.'

Mrs Darley stood up and extended her hand. 'And it's lovely to meet you, my dear, welcome to our hamlet. Would you care to join us for coffee?'

'Well I suppose my unpacking can wait,' she smiled, 'yes please, I'd be delighted.'

Once another blanket had been spread on the grass and fresh coffee prepared, we all sat down whilst Mrs Darley encouraged our temporary neighbour to tell us a little about herself.

'Well this is the perfect place for me,' Tamarind began. 'A few weeks ago I took a temporary position with the open air theatre company just a few miles from here. The following day I was in Liskeard, looking for somewhere local to stay, when I quite literally bumped into Don in the library and he helped pick me up off the floor. He offered to buy me coffee by way of an apology and told me he was going to stay with his daughter for a few months and was looking to rent his cottage out. When I discovered where it was, I almost agreed to take it before seeing it due to how convenient it would be for work, but I must admit that as soon as I actually came here to look round, I was stunned by just how beautiful it was.'

'Yes, we are lucky to live here,' said Rose. 'Tell me, what do you do down at the theatre?'

'Oh, a bit of this and a bit of that, jack of all trades and master of none really I suppose. The job was advertised as a theatre assistant, but I've since discovered that it's a description which could mean anything from standing in as an extra, to sweeping the floors. I love it though, I love the fact that it's so varied and that I get to see and listen to so many talented people and I know this might sound strange, but I like the fact that it's only temporary, which in a strange way makes it so much more exciting, knowing that you have to enjoy it right now because it's only a fleeting experience.'

'Like life,' said Mrs Darley.

'Exactly like life,' Tamarind laughed, 'love and live every moment like it's your last, that's my philosophy.'

'Oh, you'll fit in very well here, dear,' said Mrs Darley.

'Well you've all made me feel very welcome,' Tamarind replied, 'so I feel as though I fit in already.'

'Do you know, I must make the effort to come down to the theatre,' said Rose, 'I keep promising Lucy and Bod that I'll book tickets, but somehow I never seem to get round to it.'

'Then I'll make it easy for you and bring some back with me tomorrow; Peter Pan is on the week after next. In fact, why don't you all come?'

'That will be marvellous, dear,' said Mrs Darley answering for us all.

'Good. But now I will leave you all in peace and make a start on my unpacking. Thanks for the coffee.'

'Well,' said Rose as Tamarind disappeared into Don's

cottage, 'I must be going too as I promised Lucy I'd take her down to Par Market this afternoon. Anyway, I like our new inhabitant; she's like a breath of fresh air.'

'Yes,' said Mrs Darley, 'what one might call a free spirit.'

When Rose had left, Mrs Darley turned to me and said, 'And what about you, dear, what do you think about our new neighbour?'

'Initially, very nice,' I said.

'I detect a note of hesitancy.'

'No, not really, I'm just not sure whether she's my type.'

'And what is your type exactly?' asked Mrs Darley.

'Oh, I don't know,' I said.

'Well you must have an idea if you think she's not your type.'

'She just seems so ... oh, I don't know ... butterfly-like … flitting about, moving from one thing to another without any plans.'

'She offends your sensibilities and that doesn't rest easy with you?'

'It's not that it doesn't rest easy, it's just that I couldn't live my life like that.'

'Perhaps that's why Tamarind has come into your life.'

'What do you mean?' I asked.

'Sometimes, my dear, people come into our lives to mirror an aspect of ourselves that perhaps we would like to develop but which is currently lying dormant.'

'Well, there's no way I could cope with the impermanence of a temporary job, or temporary accommodation come to that,' I said.

'No, perhaps not,' said Mrs Darley, 'but maybe Tamarind's overall philosophy is worth thinking about and you never know, my dear, you may actually get to like it.'

Exploring the Senses

The senses are defined as physiological faculties, or sensory cells, through which the mind receives information about the external world, or state of the body and duly responds. They act as our interface with the world and with our inner selves whilst we are in human form.

It has been accepted throughout millennia, since Aristotle's classification of the five senses, that they comprise of our ability to touch, smell, taste, hear and see and that the nervous system has a specific sensory organ dedicated to each sense.

In more modern times, however, neurologists have found it difficult to agree on what actually constitutes a 'sense' and many consider the average human being to have many more additional senses to those defined by Aristotle and include:

Nociception (pain)

Nociception, or physical pain, signals damage in a specific area of the body. There are three types of pain receptors, namely:

1. Cutaneous (skin)
2. Somatic (joints)
3. Visceral (body organs)

Pain was once considered to be an entirely subjective experience; however in the early twentieth century it was discovered to be intertwined with all the other senses and is now known to register in the anterior cingulated gyrus of the brain.

Equilibrioception (balance and acceleration)

Equilibrioception or the vestibular sense is that which allows an organism to sense body movement, direction and acceleration and to be able to maintain postural equilibrium and balance. This is achieved through the vestibular labyrinthine system, found in both of the inner ears, which is also capable of sensing gravity.

Proprioception and Kinaesthesia (joint motor and acceleration)

Proprioception provides the parietal cortex of the brain with information on the relative position of different parts of the body. Neurologists often test this sense by asking a patient to close their eyes and touch their nose.

Thermoception (temperature differences)

Thermoception is the sense which detects heat and also the absence of heat, which we perceive to be cold. This is achieved through the thermoceptor sensors in the skin and is particularly important to a dog's sense of smell as it enables them to detect the direction of the wind and the rate of air flow.

Magnetoception (direction)

Magnetoception or magnetoroception is the sense which detects the direction in which the individual is facing based on the earth's magnetic field. It is a sense most commonly used by birds and bees, although humans do possess it in a limited form.

Sense of Time

Most neuroscientists agree that human beings do have an inbuilt - yet involved - system that governs the perception of time and includes the cerebral cortex, the cerebellum and the basal ganglia.

Some cell clusters are responsible for circadian rhythm or daily time, whilst others appear to be capable of registering shorter time ranges or ultradian rhythms both of which can malfunction in people with dementia, Parkinson's disease or attention deficit disorder.

These so-called extra senses can increase according to whether the neurologist compiling the list wishes to include *interoceptive* or internal senses, of which there are many, such as the sense of wanting to go to the toilet or the sense of wanting to swallow. Scientists, however, find it difficult to agree on what actually constitutes a sense and school is still out about the classification of various cell types and their mapping pathways to particular parts of the brain.

In cases where one sense is lost, the others become heightened as more reliance is placed upon them. The Norse god Odin, who hung upside down on the Yggdrasil tree for nine days and nine nights in search of personal transformation and enlightenment, was finally rewarded by the gods and was given the rune stones. Wounded by his own blade, he lost his sight, but in exchange was given the gift of insight as to the divinatory meanings of the runes.

Many blind people are able to 'feel' colour through their sense of touch and can detect which colours are 'warm' such as red, orange and yellow and which are cooler colours such as greens, blues and purples. This is due to the vibration of the colour itself and is particularly successful when the colour vibrations are felt through silk. Deaf people, too, often find that their sense of touch is heightened as they learn to 'hear' music through its vibration rather than its sound.

Beyond the Scientific Senses

In addition to these scientifically categorised senses there are certain human attributes to which many of us confer the word 'sense'.

A sense of fair play, a sense of decency, a sense of right and wrong, a sense of fun, a sense of adventure, sense of foreboding and a sense of obligation all fall into this category. Many of us feel, perhaps, that these qualities almost form part of the human psyche and that although they may not be identified as senses in the strict scientific meaning of the word they are things which we, as humans, are able to 'sense' somewhere deep inside our being.

The sense of humour is something with which the majority of humans are familiar and many theories exist about what humour is and exactly what function it serves, but in spite of all the research, it still remains somewhat of an enigma.

Laughter clinics have become a popular form of therapy and are frequented by those who seek relief from a myriad of disorders, including depression. This is due to the fact that laughter releases endorphins, often described as the 'feel good' hormones which help to boost the immune system.

Throughout history, many have considered humour to be a gift from the gods, an inexplicable phenomenon which takes us far beyond the mundane.

Perhaps the most mysterious of all the feelings which

we would perhaps categorise as a sense is the 'sixth' sense or a sense of knowing. It seems to arise deep within, yet to all intents and purposes there is no rational explanation as to how or from where it comes. If, however, we return for a moment to the chapter on energy and accept that everything and everyone is connected by the universal energy field, then why would it be so far removed from the realms of possibility that we are able to pick up on the energy from a world event or perhaps the thought pattern, deed or emotion of another?

Our life on this earth is a Divine mystery, yet through the five classic senses, and those of a more ethereal nature, we are not only able to experience external feelings and sensations linked solely with our physical existence, but are also able to use our senses as a medium through which to heal and, ultimately, experience the Divine.

Mrs Darley Tale: An Invitation to Heal

'Oh, dear!'

The familiar voice of Mrs Darley made me jump as I stood on the doorstep of the porch drinking a glass of water and breathing in the warm, rain filled air of a summer's evening.

'Is it so bad that you have to resort to hard drugs?'

I turned towards her somewhat puzzled, until I realised I had a packet of painkillers in my hand to accompany the water.

I smiled. 'Oh, I've just got a headache. I've had it all day, in fact I've had it on and off for a week now. I think it could be sinus problems from the pollen, or it might even be this oppressive heat. I was hoping for a thunder storm to clear the air, but I don't know whether anything will materialize,' I said peering at the sky.

'Perhaps you should look beyond the headache,' she said.

'What do you mean?' I asked.

'Come and join me,' she said and disappeared from view.

'You see, my dear,' Mrs Darley began as she handed me a peculiar hot green concoction, 'your headache hasn't just appeared because it's sultry or because there's pollen about.'

'Hasn't it?' I asked somewhat suspiciously.

Mrs Darley shook her head. 'Of course not, after all I'm breathing in the same pollen as you and I'm also living in the same thundery atmosphere, yet I have no headache.'

'Perhaps I'm just susceptible?' I suggested.

'But why?' she asked. 'Why are you susceptible and I am not?'

I shook my head. 'I don't know.'

'Well, my dear, let me offer you my thoughts on the subject of illness, regardless of its nature. You see we don't just become ill by accident, for there is always an underlying cause. We have spoken previously about the detrimental effects of not being true to *yourself*, whether this is through doing things that don't make you happy, thinking things which cause conflict or, perhaps, denying the essence of who you truly are, all of which amount to a considerable amount of stress ...'

I smiled. 'Well you could be right there!'

Ignoring my attempt at light heartedness she continued, '... when we are stressed, regardless of the area from which the stress stems, our subtle energy bodies become less vibrant, our immunity lowers and we become more susceptible to outside influences such as germs, viruses or, in your case, airborne irritants or heavy atmospheric conditions.'

'But I don't feel stressed!' I protested.

'Don't you?' she asked.

'No, I'm happy living here and happy with work.'

'But that's all you do, that's all your life consists of, simply coming home and going to work. I know we have touched upon this several times before, but your life has no balance, no joy, no creativity, in short, my dear, lack of these things is literally "doing your head in".'

I sat in silence for a moment, feeling as though she had finally slapped me into some kind of realisation, for although she and others had attempted on many occasions to point out my life's lack of balance, I had heard their words but never really listened. Phyllis' writing group was a prime example and although I had initially attended, I allowed it to peter out after three weeks due to my excuse of work commitments.

'I hope you don't think I'm interfering or criticising you,' she said leaning forward and squeezing my hand, 'but if you don't make time for yourself then you have to make time for illness.'

'I know,' I whispered, 'but I don't know what to do to change it, I always seem to have so much to do.'

'I don't accept that,' Mrs Darley said gently, 'I know you work hard, but very often I think you are so meticulous and set your standards so high that you create work for yourself, when that time could be spent doing something you enjoy. Look at your friends and work colleagues; do they spend as much time working after hours as you do?'

'Probably not.'

'And do they get penalised for it?'

I shook my head. 'No, there never seems to be much

difference between their pay rise and mine at the end of the year.'

Mrs Darley arched an eyebrow. 'And doesn't that speak volumes?' she asked.

I nodded. 'Most of them are married though and have other things to do outside of work. I think I worry that because I'm alone I have to keep my job as I don't have anyone else to rely on.'

'And that, my dear,' said Mrs Darley, 'is quite understandable. However you too deserve a life outside of work and you also owe it to yourself to keep healthy.'

I sighed, 'I can see that now.'

'Good. Now then, have you finished your drink?' She asked.

I looked at her somewhat sheepishly, as I found the colour a little off putting, 'er … no.'

'Then I will make you a fresh one,' she said disappearing into the kitchen.

She returned a few moments later with a repeat of the rather odd looking concoction.

'Will this cure my headache?' I asked.

'It will clear your thoughts, help you to see things in perspective and that in turn may help heal your headache,' she smiled.

'That seems a long winded way round when I could just take an aspirin to make the pain to go away,' I laughed.

'But then all you are doing is treating the symptom, you are not attempting to deal with the underlying cause.

'You see, my dear,' she said patiently as though speaking to a young child, 'repairing the physical body is but a small part of the healing process. Healing is a multifaceted discipline that often filters down to the very depths of the soul. When illness strikes, regardless of its severity, it comes with a message from a deeper part of our being, telling us that perhaps things aren't as harmonious as we would like to think and that some aspect of our life is not sitting peaceably.

'In your case it seems that something is "doing your head in" and, therefore, the headache comes as a gentle warning that perhaps you should think about making some changes. However, it's no good going in all guns blazing, such as dramatically reducing your working week or changing your job which, in part, you do enjoy, for that too would bring its own problems and stresses. What you need to do is think things through, consider how you intend to give yourself more time and then decide how you wish to utilise that time to bring yourself joy and pleasure, hence the tisane of mint and lemon balm.'

'Is that what it is?' I asked as I lifted the cup to my lips.

To my surprise the pale green tisane tasted rather nice and within a few minutes I had drained the cup.

'That wasn't so bad then?' Mrs Darley smiled as I placed my cup on the table.

I shook my head. 'No, actually it was good and I don't know whether it's psychological but my head actually feels a little better.'

'Well that's because the tisane has worked on both a physical and psychological level. You see, my dear, healing cannot be performed in isolation. All forms of healing work on multiple layers of our being. You cannot administer an essential oil to help heal a wound without the oil having some effect on the mind and emotions. Likewise, you cannot offer hands on healing without it touching the soul. That is why healers and wise folk refer to the mind, body, spirit connection, for each is equally important in the health and well-being of every individual.'

'I'm fascinated,' I said.

'Then perhaps you should take a journey,' she said. 'A journey of empiricism; a journey of healing through the senses.'

I smiled, as once again I felt the familiar stirrings of excitement that signified the continuance of my magickal journey.

Healing Dreamtime

Upon a ribbon of air
Sweet honeyed night stock
Snakes into my dreams,

For a moment you are mine,
Bodies entwined
As honeysuckle upon the vine.

Coveted lips speak words of love,
Which tumble like confetti
From pale scented blooms.

I taste your longing as nectar
From a lilac cup
Of sweet imaginings.

I watch you dress and mourn
The loss of your naked beauty,
As spring obscures the bough.

In my dreams I am sated.
In my dreams I am whole.
In my dreams I am healed.

Chapter 4

The Sense of Touch

The Carer
Brushing an errant hair from my face
Your hand lingers on my forehead,
Soothing, cooling.
Wiping a rogue crumb from my mouth
Your hand cups my chin,
Comforting, reassuring.
Lowering me down to sleep
Your lips brush my cheek,
Healing, life giving.

Mrs Darley Tale: Touch

There were people everywhere. Men with microphones and women with costumes bustled their way back and forth, ensuring that the peace and tranquillity I normally associated with my little row of cottages was destroyed. I sighed and eventually turned away from the bedroom window to dress.

Each year Mrs Darley and several others from the surrounding villages put on some sort of autumn play in order to raise money for the elderly at Christmas. Normally it was a wonderfully amateurish affair held in Mrs Darley's garden, with as many people as possible crammed into the space available. This year, however, was quite different and I was beginning to wish I had chosen this weekend to go and visit my parents, but it was far too late to back out and I knew there was nothing for it but to take a deep breath and volunteer my services, just as I had promised.

'Ah, there you are, dear.' The familiar voice of Mrs Darley filled me with relief as I stepped out of the porch into the bright autumnal sunshine. 'We need some help in here; Tinkerbell's wings have become detached.'

Giving an 'oh, dear' of sympathy I duly followed Mrs Darley into her cottage, which had been temporarily turned into a theatrical dressing room, filled with as many costumes and people as it would hold.

'Here we are,' said Mrs Darley gesturing towards me, 'another willing pair of hands.'

'Oh, good,' said a recognisable voice from beneath several layers of pink netting, 'it's very kind of you to come and help us. Everybody, this is my next door neighbour.'

I immediately recognised the voice as Tamarind's, the new inhabitant of the hamlet, and it was she who had offered to organise this year's event. She assured us that the actors, who had performed Peter Pan throughout the summer season at the open air theatre, would be only too pleased to do a charity event in order to give something back to the local community. Mrs Darley appeared to be delighted and, after speaking to the local farmer, had arranged for the event to be held in the field below the cottages. I for one, however, felt that the essence of what was usually a home spun event had been well and truly lost amid the formality of a professional production.

My introduction to the assembled company had caused several people in the room to lay down their needles and sequins and make a beeline for me, where I was immediately enveloped in a sea of hugs and heartfelt words of thanks.

'You look a little overwhelmed, dear,' said Mrs Darley as we stood together behind Tinkerbell, supporting the wings which were being skilfully sewn back together.

'It's all a little too "darling, darling" for my liking,' I whispered, 'I can't be doing with all this hugging, especially when I don't even know them.'

Mrs Darley smiled. 'The embracing of one human being by another is a gift of the universe. It is both healing and nourishing to the soul. Perhaps if you indulged your sense of touch a little more you would begin to enjoy it.'

I felt at a loss as to how to respond to her words and was grateful to hear Tinkerbell say, 'I think I'm OK now, thanks,' which meant I could move on to helping secure Captain Hook's hook onto his sleeve.

Later that evening, I lay in the bath and reflected on the day's events. The play, about which I had serious misgivings, was an undoubted success and the amount of money raised had quadrupled that of previous years. Tamarind had been heralded a local heroine and I was left nursing a tiny green eyed monster, that threatened to grow into unrecognisable proportions if I didn't manage to control it.

Why did I feel this jealousy towards Tamarind? Had Mrs Darley hit the nail on the head when she said that perhaps Tamarind was mirroring a part of me that was hidden and yet which longed to be brought out into the light? Did I secretly want to be held in esteem by the local community? Did I perhaps want to live a life that was less restricted, less regimented? Did I, deep down, want to be that warm open person who gave hugs freely as a gesture of acceptance and friendship?

I lay perfectly still, staring at the motionless water

when a lone droplet fell from the tap, rippling the surface and changing the energy of the bath. I suddenly remembered Mrs Darley's words, *'Once your energy changes, everything changes,'* and in that instant realised that I too could change the energy which surrounded me by becoming more open, less aloof, less controlling and, with a silent word of thanks to both Tamarind and Mrs Darley, I rose from the bath.

Sitting curled up by the fire close to ten o'clock, I was surprised to hear a knock at the door.

'Hello, dear,' said Mrs Darley as I opened the porch door. 'Sorry to call so late, but I just wanted to bring you a few bits and pieces of food that we've shared between us from the day's events, rather than letting it go to waste.'

'Thank you,' I said, 'that's much appreciated, come in and I'll make you a drink.'

'No thank you, I won't stay. It's late and I know you have work tomorrow. Oh, I almost forgot,' she said turning, 'I was asked to give you this.'

She handed me an envelope with my name boldly written across the front.

'It's a token of thanks from Tamarind, for all your help today.'

I stood in quiet contemplation for a moment before opening it and eventually pulled out a gift token for the complementary health clinic in Liskeard.

'Tamarind asked me what I thought you would like and I said you might appreciate a massage as you were interested in investigating the benefits of the sense of touch.'

I smiled at Mrs Darley's tactfully pointed way of encouraging me to experience the joys of more human contact. 'That's very kind of her,' I said, 'I've never had a massage before.'

'I know,' she said. 'Enjoy!'

Introducing the Sense of Touch

The sense of touch is the first sense to develop in the womb and is present after approximately eight weeks, enabling the foetus to feel both its watery environment and the beating of its mother's heart.

When we are born we are, if we are lucky, welcomed into the world by being cradled in our mother's arms, an act that instils within us, feelings of being loved and belonging.

To touch someone in a caring or therapeutic way is a universal instinct known by both animals and humans alike. We all understand that to give someone a hug or to rub a sore limb is, in some way, beneficial and is an activity we engage in almost subconsciously to bring comfort or relief to another or ourselves. We express parental love through the cuddling of our child and sexual love through the caressing of another.

The feel of soft or warm material against the skin gives us pleasure, which is why the majority of children form a special bond with one particular teddy bear or soft toy. To swim in a warm sea or to feel the heat of the sun upon our back all bring a sense of well-being through the power of touch.

Very often, when someone loses the use of one of their other senses, the sense of touch is heightened. The deaf can experience sound through vibration whilst the blind are able to 'see' faces and objects through touch. Reading braille through touch enables the literary world to remain a valuable part of a blind person's life.

If the pressure or force of touch is increased, then what was once a therapeutic act can quickly transform into something harmful.

At the opposite end of the spectrum, those who live their lives devoid of touch can often find themselves prone to more physical and psychological disorders, which is why the regular application of some form of therapeutic touch is beneficial to our overall health.

Today, as in times past, massage in one of its many guises, has become one of the most accepted and popular forms of therapeutic touch which, as we shall discover throughout this chapter, has many beneficial aspects.

In the words of the late Dr Thomas Stretch Dowse, an important British physician and author from Victorian days whose books such as *A Primer of the Art of Massage* are still popular:

'*The mind, which before massage is in a perturbed, restless, vacillating and even despondent state, becomes after massage, calm, quiet, peaceful and subdued; in fact, the wearied and worried mind has been converted into a mind restful, placid, and refreshed.*'

Understanding the Sense of Touch

Our sense of touch is extremely sensitive, as we are able to detect very small movements and pressures throughout our body. We have the ability to feel someone's breath upon our cheek, a money spider running across our hand, or a tiny hair in our mouth, all of which are made possible by sensitive nerve endings.

Nerve endings can be found wrapped around the base of the fine hairs of the skin and in the hairless parts of the body such as the finger tips and lips where they are embedded into tiny discs.

Those wrapped around the base of the hairs in the skin stop firing immediately if they continue to be stimulated, whereas the nerves on the hairless parts of the body continue to fire even if pressure is maintained.

The fibres responsible for conveying important touch information, such as heat and cold or pain and pleasure, send their nerve messages directly to the higher centres of the brain via the spinal cord and brainstem.

The fibres responsible for dealing with less important sensations of touch send their nerve messages on a slightly longer journey, although it too begins by entering the spinal cord.

From here these nerve messages meet a network of cells, which perform an analysis of the nerve information before sending it onwards to the brain. This analysis ensures that trivial information is suppressed, whilst the most important is transmitted. Regardless of how the sensation of touch journeys, it will eventually be transmitted to a knot of grey matter deep in the thalamus gland.

Here all the different pieces of information from various types of skin receptors are assembled and co-ordinated, which in turn, helps the brain's highest centres in the cerebral cortex, to begin to put together the sensations of touch, of which we become consciously aware.

The final picture is completed by co-ordinating the memory associated with these particular sensations with the information produced from the other senses. This can include: looking at, listening to, tasting or smelling the object touching us or being felt.

In addition, the corresponding position of the limbs, joints and digits are also taken into account, which enables us to not only determine the size and shape of an object, but also helps us to distinguish one object from another.

The History of Therapeutic Touch

To actually pinpoint the beginning of the use of therapeutic touch in healing is almost impossible. It is something that we must always have been aware of as a species and therefore all we can do is to briefly investigate how the ancient races used touch as a healing modality throughout millennia.

Although it is often thought that massage traditions in China date back some 4,000 years, there is little written proof that this was the case. The earliest Chinese documents mentioning the subject date from around 1400BC, the beginning of the Shang dynasty where the Yellow Emperor in his book *Huangdi Neijing* recommended the 'massage of skin and flesh'.

The Chinese were also well versed in two other specific 'touching' techniques which are still used today. The first was *moxa,* which involved the burning of herbs on specific skin areas in order to relieve disease, whilst the second was acupuncture, which involved the insertion of narrow needles into specific areas of the body in an attempt to block pain.

Around 100AD, documents show that Chinese students of medicine were examined in both massage and acupuncture as well as in the general treatment of bodily diseases. The first level, the *Hsiu-ts'ai* (cultivated talent) was equivalent to our BA degree; the *Ming-Ching* (understanding the classics) was equivalent to our master's degree and the *Ch'in Shih* (advanced scholar) was equivalent to our doctorate.

In contrast to the strict medical application of massage in China, Indian massage focussed more on the sensual aspect of touch with the *Kama Sutra* bearing testament to a culture that has an understanding of the power of touch in changing people's moods for the purpose of both relaxation and sexual arousal.

Hindu Tantra taught that the vital life force known as *kundalini* originated at the base of the spine and as such, this area was both soothed and stimulated with a combination of massage, breathing exercises and yogic positions.

Hippocrates, often referred to as the 'Father of Modern Medicine', utilised massage in the form of friction to treat sprains and dislocations and used kneading to ease constipation. He was credited with saying:

'*A physician must be experienced in many things but assuredly also in rubbing...for rubbing can bind a joint that is too loose and loosen a joint that is too rigid.'*

Hippocrates believed that all disease stemmed from natural causes and should therefore be treated with natural methods which included rest, diet, exercise, fresh air, massage, scented baths, music and the company of friends in order to allow the body to heal.

Asclepiades, a Roman orator and doctor of the first century BC, expounded the virtues of good food, fresh air, enemas, hydrotherapy, regular cleansing of wounds and massage in order to maintain health and was also accredited with inventing the shower bath.

The Romans were exceptionally keen on both bathing and massage and for those who could afford it, a bath followed by a massage with warm vegetable oil was the ultimate treatment for stiff muscles. Real luxury however came in the form of a full body massage, which was designed to awaken nerves, stimulate circulation and free the action of the joints. This ritual was then completed by rubbing the body with extremely fine oils, in order to keep the skin elastic and supple.

Galen, who was once physician to the Roman gladiators, advocated the use of massage in the treatment of injuries and certain diseases, recognising the effect of massage in eliminating the body's waste products.

With the decline of the Roman empire, massage became a pastime associated with the pursuit of pleasure and was often used as a substitute for exercise due to its ability to push the blood and lymph around the body, helping to counteract the effects of excessive eating and drinking.

One of the greatest eleventh century Persian medics Avicenna, or Abu Ali Al-Husayn Ibn Abd Allah Ibn Sina, to give him his correct title, often known as the 'Prince of Physicians' wrote the celebrated works *Al-Quanun fi at-tibb* (The Canon of Medicine). It has been referred to as the most famous single book in the history of medicine in both the East and West and took particular note of the use of massage in relieving pain.

Sadly for the world of medicine, Paracelsus, brilliant though he may have been as a medic, publicly burned the books of Avicenna and Galen in Basel before a crowd of cheering students in the early part of the sixteenth century. This act symbolised Paracelsus' rejection of the old ways and his preference for inorganic drugs and surgery.

The ultimate in massage techniques however, probably came from old Romania where certain illnesses were treated with what could be described as a 'type of massage', as the patient concerned was trodden on by a tame bear.

Although the ancient civilizations were well versed in the use of massage, the honour of bringing a more structured form of massage to the Western world is given to the nineteenth century Swedish doctor, Dr Per Henrik Ling.

Ling combined gymnastic movements with massage techniques, borrowed from many of the ancient cultures and formed a type of massage therapy that is now often referred to as 'Swedish Massage'. Ling is quoted as saying:

'We ought not to consider the organs of the body as then lifeless forms of a mechanical mass, but as the living, active instruments of the soul.'

In the 1890s a society of trained masseuses was formed in Britain in order to increase the standard of massage training, and in 1899 Sir William Bennet introduced a massage department into St George's Hospital, London.

The popularity of using massage techniques within a hospital environment grew beyond recognition and resulted in St Thomas's Hospital having a dedicated massage department until 1934. As modern medicine advanced, electrical stimulation of muscles and organs superseded that of manual massage.

During the first half of the twentieth century, Willhelm Reich, a psychiatrist and contemporary of Freud, made an association between muscular tensions and knots and the suppression of sexual and emotional feelings. These pioneering thoughts led him to introduce massage into his psychiatry sessions, an act which not only outraged society, but resulted in him becoming alienated from the classical psychoanalytical movement.

Apart from a brief interlude where massage was primarily associated with the seedier side of life, Reich's fate did little to suppress the growing need for massage as a healing modality and, during the latter half of the twentieth century, massage training became very popular, leading to almost every town in Britain offering some form of massage therapy within a complementary health or beauty clinic.

Today massage is used therapeutically in hospitals and care homes, benefiting cancer patients, premature babies, dementia sufferers and those recovering from heart attacks and strokes. Health clinics also offer massage therapy to those who live with chronic pain or who are recovering from drug abuse.

Understanding Massage

The word 'massage' has conflicting origins. One school of thought says that it derives from the French word, 'massage' meaning 'friction' or 'kneading', another is that it comes from the Arabic 'massa', meaning 'to touch, feel or handle', whilst a third suggestion is that it derives from the Latin word 'massa', meaning 'mass or dough'. Despite the word's true origins, massage has something to offer everyone and is a healing art in its own right.

In simple terms, massage involves the manipulation of the superficial layers of muscle and connective tissue of the body in order to bring about a myriad of benefits, both physiological and psychological.

There are, in fact, over eighty different types of therapy that fall under the massage umbrella, with the majority involving specific movements such as stretching, petrissage, effleurage, pressures, rolling, brushing and occasionally yogic positions, all of which are delivered through the hands, fingers, feet, knees or forearms according to the amount of pressure required.

In the west, massage is most often performed on a couch, although massage chairs are popular for 'on site' massage treatments where a therapist may go into a company and offer employees shorter treatments. In some eastern forms of massage such as Thai or shiatsu, couches are rejected in favour of the floor, as these therapies are quite physical and involve the therapist moving the client's body into different positions rather than having them lie stationary upon a couch.

Regardless of the type chosen however, massage offers us a non-verbal way of communicating with another human being and is capable of touching us on an extremely deep level.

The Beneficial Effects of Massage

Research has shown that the benefits of massage are manyfold against few contraindications and that therapeutic touch is able to affect us on all levels of our being. To have an understanding of this, we must look at the work of a neuroscientist called Candace Pert. Dr Pert, formerly chief of the Brain Biochemistry Section at the American National Institute of Mental Health and now professor at the Centre for Molecular and Behavioural Neuroscience at Rutgers University, is affectionately known as 'The Goddess of Neuroscience', having won the respect of both orthodox science and the complementary world.

Dr Pert has shown through her pioneering work, outlined in her autobiography, *The Molecules of Emotion*, that the subconscious is not only held in the mind, but also within every cell of the body. The immune system contains the same peptides as those found within the brain and works in conjunction with the nervous and endocrine systems, forming an important network of communication. The carriers of information between these various systems are called 'neuropeptides', which, along with their receptors, form the biochemical basis for feeling and have earned the title of 'the molecules of emotion'.

Therapeutic touch not only brings about benefits on a physical level, but is also capable of releasing repressed feelings and emotions which have become embedded deep within the cells of the body.

There are many other benefits of therapeutic touch, which assist in our overall well-being and help to:

- Reduce muscular knots and tension.
- Tone and firm muscles.
- Reduce pain and inflammation.
- Reduce mobility difficulties.
- Stimulate cell renewal, which helps to speed recovery time around an injury site.
- Warm muscles before attempting any sports activities and aid their relaxation afterwards.
- Stimulate the circulatory system and encourage blood flow to all parts of the body.
- Increase the flow of lymph around the body. The lymphatic system, unlike the circulatory system, has no equivalent to the heart in order to pump the lymph around the body. Therefore, if we fail to move around, either through laziness or illness, then the lymph remains stagnant, causing toxins to build up in the body. Massage ensures that the lymph is moved to the drainage points where toxins can pass easily away.
- Breakdown cellulite.
- Bring about the sought after relaxing 'alpha state' and, on occasions, the deeper 'theta state', both of which calm breathing patterns, kick-start the body's natural healing system and relieve

anxious and depressive states.

- Release endorphins into the blood stream bringing about the 'feel good factor' and acting as a stress reliever.
- Increase the levels of oxytocin in the brain. Oxytocin is a hormone that is usually associated with childbirth as it encourages milk production, eases labour and is responsible in part, for the strong emotion that is experienced by the mother when she sees her child for the first time.

  Due to research carried out in the 1990s, oxytocin was shown to be present in both men and women and is produced in high levels when we fall in love, making us more loving and generous towards others.

  Scientific trials have proved that oxytocin is a powerful antioxidant, preventing free radical damage, a key factor in the cause of up to sixty major diseases. It also prevents premature ageing, reduces inflammation and stress levels, helps to restore lost sleep patterns and plays a key role in keeping the arteries supple and healthy, thereby reducing heart disease. When we are hugged, stroke a pet, or are touched in a caring or therapeutic way, the levels of oxytocin rise dramatically.
- Build up trust between client and therapist
- Bring into focus the powerful sense of touch without having to give anything in return.

Massage improves every organ of the body and assists the body in the stimulation and optimum function of all its systems, despite the fact that it does not actually 'do' anything to the body itself.

Being aware of the Contraindications of Massage

Any massage therapist worth their salt will complete a health related questionnaire before beginning any form of body therapy treatment, as there are certain medical conditions that are contraindicated with a full body massage, although this does not necessarily exclude localised areas.

Conditions which may be contraindicated include: certain types of cancer, severe heart conditions, fever, infectious disease, phlebitis, deep vein thrombosis, newly formed scar tissue, inflamed, strained or swollen areas, circulatory disorders and lymphoedema (unless attending a fully trained practitioner).

Massage is often best avoided in the following circumstances, due to its action upon the mind and the physical body:

- After eating a heavy meal as it can feel very uncomfortable.
- Following the consumption of alcohol as massage can speed up the absorption process, often resulting in feelings of nausea or intoxication.
- If the need to feel awake or alert is important.

Types of Massage

Today there are over eighty types of recognised body therapy in use throughout the world. Table 1.6, below, provides a snapshot of the most popular, including how they are applied and their associated benefits.

Type of Massage	Description
Acupressure / Acupuncture	Acupressure and acupuncture both utilise the same 'junctions' on the meridian system in order to release

	blocked energy. The difference is that acupressure uses finger pressure whilst acupuncture uses fine needles.
Aromatherapy Massage	Combines gentle massage techniques with the use of essential oils to promote health and well-being.
Ayurvedic Massage	Of Indian origins, this utilises the ayurvedic system of humours (vatta, pitta, kapha) which incorporate yoga, meditation and herbal remedies along with a type of massage called 'Abhyanga', usually performed by two therapists simultaneously.
Bowen Therapy	This technique, invented by Tom Bowen in the twentieth century, involves gentle rolling movements over the connective tissue or fascia to help the realignment of the body and the release of energy blocks, which in turn, help to ease pain and tension.
Lymphatic Drainage Massage	A specialist massage used for those suffering from lymphodema, often caused by the removal of the lymph glands in sufferers of breast cancer, or those who are unable to move due to a medical condition.
Reiki	Usually described as a 'hands on healing technique', reiki is far more than this and can lead to personal development, spiritual progression and the ability to connect with a Divine essence. Reiki can also be administered via the auric field and can be 'sent' to those who are unable to reach a practitioner.
Reflexology	Utilises thumb and finger pressure on the reflex points of the feet (which mirror the whole body) to assist in correcting physical and energetic imbalances.
Remedial Massage	Helps to restore function to injured muscles, tendons and ligaments

	through a variety of classic massage movements.
Sports Massage	Combines many massage techniques to enhance sports performance and recuperation from injury.
Shiatsu	An eastern therapy, which uses a combination of finger pressures, in the same way as acupressure, but also incorporates stretching, grasping, rolling and brushing moves.
Stone Massage	A treatment which uses stones to apply pressure and varying degrees of heat to the body. The stones can also be coated with oil and used to perform various massage strokes. The heated stones penetrate the muscles helping to release muscular tension whilst the cold stones help with swelling and inflammation.
Swedish Massage	Swedish massage brings the body back into balance by utilising a combination of five relaxing and stimulating movements: Effleurage (gliding), Petrissage (kneading), Tapotement (tapping), Frictions (cross fibre movements), Vibrations (gentle shaking). It is helpful in reducing pain, stiffness, stimulating poor circulation and bringing about feelings of relaxation.
Thai Massage	Thai massage originated in India and is based on a combination of ayurvedic and yoga techniques. It is usually performed on the floor due to the nature of the stretching moves.

Table 1.6

Touching the Emotions

Our ability to feel and touch often extends far beyond the physical sense and takes us hurtling into the realm of the emotions. We use the verb 'to touch' or 'to feel' frequently in our language in order to describe our emotional state. This may be in a positive sense, such as when we feel happy or ecstatic, or it may be used in a negative way when we become overwhelmed by life and perhaps feel sad, empty or afraid. The phrase 'I am touched' is often used when we are moved by an act of kindness or we might say 'I feel very touchy about that subject' when someone is getting close to making us feel emotional about a particular situation.

This emotional association with our sense of touch is quite understandable, as our emotional state is literally felt in the physical body as discussed earlier in this chapter through the findings of Dr Candice Pert. We therefore attempt to equate how we feel by associating the feeling with a particular part of the body as illustrated below:

- I'm so sad, my heart is broken.
- I'm so nervous; I have butterflies in my stomach.
- I'm so lost without him / her I feel as though I've had my right arm cut off.
- I'm so happy, I feel as though my feet have wings.

There are occasions when those who have developed their psychic abilities are able to detect a little about the owner of an object simply by holding it and feeling its vibrations, a gift known in psychic circles as *clairsentience*, meaning to have 'clear feelings'. This is also commonly better known as psychometry.

Dedication

For me, the sense of touch reminds me that I am human. It is the sense through which I can experience earthly and earthy pleasures.

To make love, to swim in the sea, to dance, to fly, to hold a child, to stroke a pet, to comfort someone in distress, to give or receive a reiki treatment, to walk the wild land, to sit beside a blazing fire, to feel the sun on my back or iced fingers of snow upon my cheek, all of these things and more remind me of my connectedness to the element of earth.

The following dedication to the *Goddess* is an example of how we can express our appreciation for our sense of touch. Light a green or pink candle, symbolic of the heart centre and the earth; place an object of home made craftwork produced through the sense of touch beside the candle, such as a painting, needlework, or a flower arrangement and chant the following dedication:

Lady Goddess, gift bearer of the senses,
I appreciate and honour my sense of touch.
I give thanks that I am able to feel nature's elements against my cheek,
I give thanks that I am able to hold out my hand to both give and receive friendship,
I give thanks that I may both give and receive healing through loving touch.
Please accept this piece of craftwork as token of my gratitude.

Let the candle burn right down if possible. It may be a generous gesture to give the handmade item away to someone as a gift, or perhaps help someone out in a practical way such as giving a hand massage, doing the washing up or mowing the lawn; any act which engages the sense of touch.

Conclusion

It becomes easy to understand that our sense of touch and our ability to feel can affect us on many levels. By taking time out to experience some form of therapeutic touch, whether it is in the form of a massage or a hug, can benefit not only the physical body but have a profound effect on our overall well-being.

Touch is a simple, precious gift. It brings balance to mind, body and spirit and offers a sense of completeness.

Mrs Darley Tale: Arachne

I was standing on a stool cleaning my lounge window when Lucy came strolling round the path.

'Hello', she called.

'Oh, hello, Lucy,' I replied, 'are you going to see Mrs 'D'?'

Lucy nodded. 'I'm bored,' she said, 'so I just wondered if she wanted to go for a walk. Would you like to come?' she asked.

'Do you know, I think I might,' I said. 'I've had enough of cleaning windows.'

'So,' Mrs Darley asked as we made our way up on to the lane, 'where shall we go?'

'Up to the railway track,' said Lucy, 'I like it up there and then we can follow the track to the village and I can get sweets from the shop.'

'Ah,' said Mrs Darley, 'so there is an alternative motive to this walk?'

Lucy smiled. 'Don't tell Mum about the sweets, she says I've got to cut down after having two fillings last week.'

'And don't you think that might be a good idea?' asked Mrs Darley.

Lucy shrugged and adopted an unusually grumpy

look.

'Look,' said Mrs Darley, 'how about you forgoing the sweets, which means that none of us have to lie to your mother and I'll treat us to a cream tea instead at the café?'

Lucy perked up immediately, 'OK,' she agreed and, with matters concerning sweet offerings settled, we finally set off towards the railway track.

As we climbed ever upward amongst the waist high ferns, a hazy sun gradually began to appear and the day suddenly became very warm. Our walk was disturbed by a shout from Lucy who had run ahead and called us to follow.

'Look!' she said as we caught her up.

Bending down beside her we were intrigued to see a tiny snake, which was obviously making the most of the summer sunshine.

'What is it?' Lucy asked.

'An adder,' replied Mrs Darley, 'you can tell by the diamond patterns down its back, mind you it's only a baby. How lovely to see one, I expect it's an ideal habitat here on this dry track and in this heat. We must be careful though not to inadvertently disturb any, especially the adults.'

'I'll avoid them by climbing up here,' said Lucy, beginning to make her way over the large boulders which had tumbled down from the now disused quarry.'

'Well be careful,' said Mrs Darley, 'and watch your footing.'

No sooner were the words out of her mouth, we heard Lucy cry out in pain as her foot slipped between the rocks.

'Oh, dear,' called Mrs Darley, 'Lucy, are you alright?'

'I've cut my foot,' she said.

'Can you climb down?' Mrs Darley asked.

'Don't worry,' I said, 'I'll climb up and get her.'

The cut on Lucy's toe looked quite nasty as she removed her canvas shoe and I quickly wrapped a tissue around it as a temporary measure until I got her back down to the track.

'It's rather a deep cut,' I said to Mrs Darley as I lowered Lucy onto the ground.

'Mmmm,' murmured Mrs Darley, pulling away the tissue and peering at the toe in question, 'but I think I know something that just might help.'

Intrigued, Lucy and I watched as she walked back towards the boulders and appeared to be searching for something amongst the rocks. Obviously finding what she was looking for, she turned and came back grasping something in her hand.

'Now then,' she said opening up her closed hand, 'this should hold things together until we get home.'

To my surprise, she began to wrap Lucy's cut toe with a piece of spider's web.

'Yuk,' said Lucy, 'that's horrible!'

'Shush, dear,' said Mrs Darley, 'it's better than walking around with a gaping toe, especially as we've still got a quarter of a mile to go until we get to the village. When we get there we'll phone your mum and ask her to come and pick us up, although I'm afraid you'll have to forgo your cream tea.'

Lucy looked as though she might protest, but obviously thinking better of it, remained quiet.

I took advantage of her silence in order to ask Mrs Darley a question, 'Why a spider's web?'

'Because it's an age-old remedy that's been used for thousands of years to bind wounds together. In addition to its stickiness, it's also thought to have antiseptic properties and, in the absence of anything else, it's worth a try. I remember my grandfather using it once on my brother's leg when he sliced it on a fishing hook.'

'How amazing,' I said as Lucy slipped her blood soaked shoe back on and began to hobble along towards the village.

At long last, after being rescued by Rose, we all found ourselves back in Mrs Darley's cottage where she and Rose tended to Lucy's foot by soaking it in a bowl of warm water infused with a mixture of tea tree and lavender oils.

'There,' said Mrs Darley, 'that should soon kick-start the healing process.'

'I'd never have thought of using a spider's web as a means of a plaster,' said Rose, 'but I can see just how useful it can be. I just hope the spider didn't mind too much at having her web destroyed.'

'Oh, spiders are quite used to spinning and re-spinning their webs,' said Mrs Darley as she dried off Lucy's foot and wound a plaster around the offending toe. 'The Greek goddess Athene (called 'Athena' by both Greeks and Romans) saw to that.'

'How?' I asked, emerging from the kitchen with four cups of hot chocolate made at Mrs Darley's request.

'Well,' she began, 'Athene was a powerful warrior goddess, born of Zeus after he swallowed his wife, Metis.'

'Good lord!' said Rose, 'these gods had some very odd practices!'

'Indeed, my dear,' smiled Mrs Darley, 'anyway Athene was a woman of many talents, for not only was she a warrior goddess who protected and defended the brave, she also excelled beyond measure in the crafts of spinning and weaving and it was these skills which led to the story I am about to tell.

'In a place called Lydia, there lived a young mortal woman called Arachne; she was also renowned for her spinning and weaving skills.

'One day Arachne made the mistake of challenging Athene to a spinning and weaving competition. Upon receiving the challenge, Athene, disguised as an old woman, visited Arachne and asked her to withdraw her ridiculous challenge, saying that she stood no chance of winning the competition against a goddess. Arachne, however, refused, and immediately began to spin her thread and weave it upon her loom, choosing to produce a beautiful piece of cloth depicting the loves of the gods.

'When it was finished she submitted it to Athene for inspection and although the goddess tried as hard as she could to find some imperfection, she was unable to do so and, in a jealous rage, she changed Arachne into a spider. Not satisfied with this cruel act, Athene condemned Arachne to eternally spin, and draw from her own body, the thread with which she was to weave her web.

'So you see, my dears, the spider will always re-spin its web regardless of how many time it is destroyed.'

'So that's where arachnophobia comes from,' I said, 'the fear of spiders.'

'Indeed it does,' said Mrs Darley.

'Fascinating,' I mused.

My musings, however, were soon interrupted by Rose standing up and saying to Lucy, 'Well, missy, say your thank yous to these kind ladies and we'll go and see what we can find for dinner and, while dinner's cooking, I might just run you up to the shop and let you choose some sweets as a treat.'

Mrs Darley winked at Lucy. 'Isn't it interesting how things turn out, dear?' she said.

Reiki

I feel your fear,
I sense your pain,
Too delicate to be manipulated,
Yet still I touch you.

You lie motionless,
Breaking my heart,
Until morphine heralds sweet oblivion,
Yet still I touch you.

Peace descends.
You are free,
No longer bound by earthly chains,
Yet still I touch you.

Chapter 5

The Sense of Smell

Cestrum Nocturnum (Lady of the Night)
Honeyed sweetness drugs the senses,
Jasmine weights the warm night air,
Gentle night stock breathes her perfume,
Let me tempt you with my wares.

Tumbled scent of evening primrose,
Mignonette and moonflower vine,
Let the fragrance of my chamber,
Weave a charm as strong as wine.

Silver ghosts and scented catchfly,
Mask your scent and hide your shame,
Come into my fragranced boudoir,
You, my moth and I, your flame.

Mrs Darley Tale: Lavender

It was Phyllis's birthday and a party was in full swing at Mrs Darley's cottage. A myriad of beautiful flowers hung from every beam in the lounge and the cottage was filled with the delicate perfume of midsummer blooms. Lively folk music blared out from a tape recorder in the corner and the slate hearth housed a neatly stacked pile of logs with which to feed the late evening's fire.

The sound of a bell momentarily halted proceedings as Mrs Darley called from the kitchen door, 'Food!'

There was a murmur of approval as we all began to file into the tiny kitchen in order to partake of Mrs Darley's culinary summer delights and to fill our glasses with a rather pale looking liquid contained within an elegant glass bowl.

'Oh, there's something about the smell of this,' said Eddie as he ladled the liquid out into his glass, 'that's taken me right back to a particularly foggy night during my childhood,'

'Some sweet goodies made by your granny no doubt?' smiled Phyllis.

'No, nothing to do with Granny, although Mother and I did live with her in those days on the outskirts of Bodmin. No, the occasion I've just thought of was rather an odd one and was triggered by the smell of Mrs D's strange concoction.'

'I'm not sure quite what you mean by my "strange concoction",' she smiled, 'it's a lavender tisane actually, but as smell is the only sense connected directly to the brain the memories evoked by aromas are particularly powerful. So tell us, Eddie, what past memories have been stirred by my aromatic kitchen?'

'Well, it was a dark foggy night, sometime before Christmas I seem to recall, because we had just been to visit Great Aunt Elsie and we only ever went there at that time of year to wish her compliments of the season. Anyway, the bus we had been waiting for didn't turn up, so mother decided we would have to walk.'

'Was it far?' asked Phyllis.

'Well, it was to me then,' said Eddie, 'I was only little in those days.'

'I find it difficult to believe that you were ever little!' laughed Peter.

'Well, a bit smaller than I am now at any rate,' Eddie

smiled. 'Anyway, as we were walking home, the fog grew increasingly thick and although we'd followed what we thought was the lane out of town, we found ourselves, after half an hour or so, at what seemed to be a dead end. To make matters worse, my mother had stumbled and was limping in pain with her ankle'

'You must have turned off the main road somewhere,' said Bod.

'Well I can't ever remember us straying from the lane, although I'll grant you that time plays tricks on the memory, but my mother always maintained that we were led that night by some strange force, for the dead end road is not the end of the story.'

'How exciting,' said Phyllis, 'do go on.'

'Just as we were about to turn around and retrace our steps a man's voice called to us from out of the darkness and asked us in a thick Cornish accent, "Are 'ee lost?"

'My mother immediately pulled me close to her and explained that we must have taken the wrong turning in the fog and that we were just about to retrace our steps.

'The man, whose features I found difficult to make out in the dark, said, "Ee's a long way from the main road 'ere."

'My mother said we couldn't be that far away as we had only left Bodmin half an hour ago and although she tried to remain calm, I can remember, even at my young age, detecting a slight note of panic in her voice and in that instant I felt afraid.

'The man, however, was quite insistent that we were much further from the road than we thought and invited us into his cottage for a warm drink saying it would keep the damp out on such a cold foggy night and that Mrs Tregarrow always had a pot on the fire for an occasion such as this.

'Mother, though, shook her head, thanked him for his offer, but said that we had to get back and, taking my hand firmly in hers, we turned and began to walk away. However, we'd only walked a few yards when she went over on her ankle again and before we knew where we were, we found ourselves being taken into the Tregarrow's cottage.

'Now as I've said, I wasn't very big in those days, but even I had to stoop beneath the lintel that sagged across the doorway in order to enter the cottage. Once inside it was like stepping into the past. I remember the slate floor being strewn with straw and a huge cooking pot hanging over the roaring fire, which reminded me of a cauldron.

'Mrs Tregarrow indicated that we should sit alongside the fire on a hard, high-backed settle, whilst she filled a small wooden bowl with water from a pitcher on the table. I remember her telling Mr Tregarrow to take down a bunch of herbs that were hanging from the beams, some of which she broke away from their stems and sprinkled them into the bowl. She then took a piece of cloth from a drawer in the dresser, tore it into strips and soaked them in the bowl.

'As she bound my mother's foot and covered it with what looked like an old knitted sock of Mr Tregarrow's, she said, "This will ease the pain and bring down the swelling in no time, my dear".'

'What was it that she put in the water?' asked Phyllis, 'do you know?'

'Well, that's the strange thing, I didn't know, not until tonight, when I went into the kitchen and took the lid off that lavender tisane and all the memories of that night came flooding back.'

'How interesting,' said Mrs Darley, 'because lavender is one of Mother Nature's most precious gifts to humankind.'

'I just thought it was good for spots and insomnia,' said Rose, 'what else does it do?'

'Oh, numerous things,' said Mrs Darley raising her glass of lavender tisane. 'Lavender has the ability to heal on many levels. Spiritually it affects the whole spectrum of the human energy field, psychologically it calms and soothes whilst on a physical level, and as you so rightly say, Rose, it helps with spots and insomnia but it can also reduce pain and swelling, as was the case for your mother's sprained ankle, Eddie.'

'It all sounds too good to be true,' said Peter, 'are you saying that lavender has no shadow side?'

'Oh, Peter, everything has a shadow side,' laughed Mrs Darley. 'Lavender is a no, no for those with low blood pressure and for those who are in the first trimester of pregnancy.'

'Why?' asked Rose, 'I thought lavender was good to use in pregnancy for back ache and such like?'

'It is, my dear, it is, but only during the second and third trimester, when all danger of miscarriage has passed. Lavender is an 'emmenagogue', which means that it encourages menstrual bleeding, something of course that no one wants during the first stages of pregnancy.'

'Who'd have thought that Eddie's story of a mysterious walk in the fog would have led to a lesson in the healing properties of lavender,' laughed Phyllis. 'Anyway, Eddie, is there any more to your story and did you ever get home?'

'Well, with my mother's ankle bandaged, Mrs Tregarrow turned her attention to the pot over the fire and ladled out two bowls of what tasted like chicken broth, which she recommended for speeding the healing of any torn ligaments and to keep out the cold.

'With both of us feeling much better for the Tregarrow's kindness, we set out on the road once again and, although my mother's ankle should have hampered our progress, before we knew it we were turning down the narrow lane to our cottage.

'Over the week that followed, my mother sat each evening and embroidered a small hanging plaque inscribed with the words "thank you for your kindness", which she intended to take to the Tregarrow's as a token of her appreciation the very next time we went into Bodmin. However, try as we might over the weeks that followed, we simply could not find their cottage. We took every turn on that road out of Bodmin and yet the Tregarrow's cottage never materialised.'

'You must have been on a completely different road to where you thought you were,' said Peter.

Eddie shook his head. 'We couldn't have been, because we found our way home so easily.'

'Yes, but the years play tricks on your mind, and you were only young,' said Peter.

'Oh, Peter,' said Phyllis, 'don't try and come up with a logical explanation. I was quite enjoying the mystery of it all.'

'Well,' said Bod, who up until then had remained uncharacteristically quiet, 'I've spent most of my life out and about in many parts of the world, and over the years I've heard some rather strange tales of a similar ilk to the one you have just mentioned, where places have manifested for a particular reason and then seemingly disappeared, so I for one don't doubt your story.'

'And neither do I,' said Mrs Darley. 'Don't they say that when the student is ready the master will appear and, in a similar way, when the patient is ready the healer too will appear; often, my dear Peter,' she said smiling and squeezing his hand, 'without the need for a logical explanation.'

Introducing the Sense of Smell

The sense of smell is the second sense to develop in the womb and is normally present in the unborn child at between eleven and fifteen weeks. It is one of the most ancient and subtle of the senses and although, in the human species, it is considered inferior to that of many animals it is, nevertheless, capable of carrying out a myriad of functions, all of which are vitally important to our safety and well-being.

Smell is not simply a biological and psychological experience; it is also a social and cultural phenomenon. Often when people in the west are asked which of the senses they would rather manage without if they were forced to choose just one, the majority opt for the sense of smell. Smell has, therefore, become the most undervalued of the senses in the modern world, yet cultural historians have shown that this was not always the case and was something that was sadly brought about through the 'revaluation of the senses' by philosophers and scientists of the eighteenth and nineteenth centuries.

During this period, sight was considered to be the superior sense, whilst smell was seen as a sense of the lower orders, being in alignment with primitive savagery and even madness. The emotions that smell evoked were thought to threaten the rational detachment of modern scientific thinking and these opinions dominated academic research for almost two centuries, leading us to know less about the sense of smell than the other more respected senses.

Even our language associated with smell is

derogatory. We refer to the nose as a 'hooter,' 'snout,' 'beak,' 'snozzle,' 'conk,' or 'snitch', whilst smells that are not perceived as pleasant are described as a 'pong,' 'stink,' 'honk,' or 'whiff'. The verb 'to smell' has a derogatory meaning, unless qualified as something pleasant by adding an appropriate adjective such as lovely or nice. Referring to just 'a smell' infers that the aroma is not quite as pleasant as it might be.

We use the language of smell to describe the way we feel about many things. Something we might intuit as not being quite right and say that we can 'smell a rat'. On a more positive note, we might 'sniff out a bargain' at the shops, almost as though we feel we have been divinely guided towards a specific product. We might say that a free gift is 'not to be sniffed at', whilst someone we may find irritating, we would perhaps describe as 'getting up our nose'.

Regardless of our often less than complementary references towards smell, the study of olfaction is, today, reasserting its importance and attracting the attention of anthropologists, sociologists and historians, whilst the practice of aromatherapy has brought the powerful effects of smell into the public domain.

In non-western cultures, however, smell has, throughout the ages, earned far more respect. In the Andaman Islands in Indonesia, the Ongee people define everything in their world and, indeed, the Universe by smell. Their calendar is constructed according to the smell of the flowers that come into bloom at different times of the year. Each season is named after a particular odour and is thought to possess its own distinctive 'aroma force'.

When in conversation, a person will touch the end of his or her nose when referring to themselves in a gesture which means, 'me and my odour'.

When greeting a friend they will ask, 'Konyune onorange-tanka?' meaning, 'how is your nose?' The person being greeted replies in one of two ways; either that they are 'heavy with odour', at which point the greeter takes a deep breath in order to remove some of the surplus. On the other hand, they may reply that they are 'short of odour' at which point the greeter will blow on the person being greeted in order to provide them with more odour energy.

The Bororo people of Brazil and the Serer-Ndut of Senega associate a person's body odour with the quality of their life-force and associate a person's breath odour with the quality of their soul energy.

They therefore claim to be able to detect which ancestor has been reincarnated into a child by the similarity in smell of the child's breath to that of a deceased ancestor.

In India, the once equivalent affectionate greeting to our hug or kiss was to smell someone's head. An ancient Indian text declared: 'I will smell thee on the head, that is the greatest sign of tender love.'

Smell is therefore an extremely undervalued sense, yet without this precious gift, our lives would be decidedly poorer on many levels, a fact that will become evident as this chapter unfolds.

The History of Aromatic Substances in Healing

The use of plants in healing is almost as old as time itself and one of the earliest forms of using plant material was by way of burning it and inhaling the aromatic smoke which arose from the fire. Indeed, fragrant smoke was considered so precious to ancient man that he often made offerings of aromatic incenses to the gods, a practice which has continued within many religions up to the present day.

The ancient Egyptians used aromatic plant materials in their cosmetics, the embalming of the dead, flavourings in medicines and in an extremely elaborate ritual of appeasing their Sun god, Ra.

At dawn they would go to Ra's temple and offer frankincense; at midday, myrrh and at sundown the infamous Egyptian perfume *Kyphi.*

Kyphi was the most revered of all Egyptian aromatics and could contain up to sixteen different ingredients which included: myrrh, honey, juniper, cardamom, turpentine and calamus. Calamus is now known to be extremely toxic and carcinogenic, but was once used for its ability to bring about powerful narcotic effects.

The Greeks learned much of their knowledge from the Egyptians, but did make discoveries of their own, including which aromatic oils were good for inducing sleep or which would stimulate the brain.

The renowned Greek medic Hippocrates, often referred to as 'the father of modern medicine', frequently recommended aromatic baths to his patients, a fact that did not go unnoticed by the well respected modern day aromatherapist Patricia Davis, founder of the London School of Aromatherapy, when she was quoted as saying:

'If they (doctors) were taught some of Hippocrates' methods the world of medicine would be in less of a mess!'

In Roman times, Galen, who later became the surgeon to Marcus Aurelius, began his career as surgeon to a school of gladiators. In the writings of the day it was noted that whilst he had responsibility for the health of the gladiators, not one died of his wounds and that a bottle of scented myrrh was always on hand to treat any injuries that occurred.

Other parts of the world also contributed to what we now know as aromatherapy, for the Indians were also using oils at the same time as the Egyptians and Greeks in a form of medicine known as Ayurveda (the ancient Indian philosophy of health and well-being). This particular modality incorporated the use of massage with over 700 substances, including many aromatics such as: cinnamon, spikenard, ginger, myrrh coriander and sandalwood.

Around 1000 AD, in the Middle East, emerged a great physician, whom we met in the previous chapter and was popularly known as Avicenna. Avicenna studied all the natural sciences of the day, but it was his interest in alchemy that led to the first refined production of distilled oils by his invention of a refrigerated coil. It is said that his first distillation was of 'Rosa Centifolia' (Rose Maroc or Rose absolute) as he was attempting to isolate the soul of the holy rose of Islam.

Avicenna, however, may not have been the first person to distil essential oils, for in 1975 Dr Paolo Rovesti led an archaeological expedition to Pakistan where, at the foot of the Himalayas, he discovered a perfectly preserved still made of terracotta. Alongside it stood several perfume containers, verifying its use in the preparation of aromatic oils some 4,000 years before Avicenna's refinement.

The Bible too gives many examples of the use of fragrant herbs and spices. When the Jews began their Exodus from Egypt, around 1240 BC, they took with them many precious gums and resins. According to the

Book of Exodus 30:32, the Christian God advised Moses how to blend oils with which to anoint Aaron into priesthood:

'Then the Lord said to Moses, "Take the following fine spices: 500 shekels of liquid myrrh, half as much of fragrant cinnamon, 250 shekels of fragrant cane, 500 shekels of cassia- all according to the sanctuary shekel- and a hin (4 litres) of olive oil. Make these into a fragrant blend, the work of a perfumer. It will be the sacred anointing oil".'

Following the rise of Christianity in the fourth century, the use of perfumes and aromatic plants was considered decadent. Herbal remedies and essential oils were therefore driven underground, where they were still used by wise women and cunning men for the purpose of magickal potions and healing.

During the Middle Ages, aromatic herbs did begin to make a comeback. Due to the problems of sanitation and various types of plague, the authorities instructed bonfires of aromatic woods to be lit in order to purify the air. Doctors, meanwhile, recommended aromatic fires to be burned in the home, herbs to be placed by the windows and a mixture of rosewater and vinegar to be placed on the floor. These ideas, though, were far from new, as Hippocrates had burned scented stakes in Athens many centuries before in an attempt to combat the plague.

Doctors themselves wore nosebags filled with aromatic herbs, through which they breathed to protect themselves, whilst many people would carry oranges stuck with cloves or carry bouquets of aromatic herbs known as *tussie mussies*.

It was noted during one outbreak of the plague that a particular group of people appeared to have immunity, the majority of which worked in a glove factory where essential oil of juniper was used to tan the leather.

By the seventeenth century, with the process of distillation well developed, essential oils began to form part of a traditional herbalist's remedies, as is illustrated in Nicholas Culpeper's *Complete Herbal* written in1653: 'The chymical (sic) drawn from the leaves and flowers is a sovereign help.'

During this period many ailments were treated with aromatic herbs and oils including: hysteria, amenorrhea, melancholia, hypochondria, headaches and colds.

From this point on, herbalists and doctors of the time would use plant extracts and oils right up until the nineteenth century, when modern medicine as we understand it today began to come to the fore. At this time, interests switched from purely natural medicines to those that were chemically produced and which isolated the 'bit that worked', rather than using the whole plant or oil.

In 1910 (some sources quote 1920), Rene Maurice Gattefosse rediscovered the healing properties of lavender whilst carrying out some laboratory experiments in which he burnt his hand quite badly. He immediately plunged it into the nearest bowl of liquid, which happened to be lavender oil. He documented the results, which not only stated that he healed remarkably quickly, but also that there was an absence of scarring. He went on to recommend the use of essential oils in the treatment of First World War soldiers.

At the same time there were other doctors and writers who also began to appreciate the healing properties of essential oils, one of whom was Dr A Penfold, an

Australian doctor. Dr Penfold began to experiment with tea tree oil, which had been known as an antiviral and antibacterial in its natural form to the Aborigines for thousands of years.

During the Indochina War (also known as the French Indochina War) of December 19, 1946, until August 1, 1954, Dr Jean Valnet continued Dr Penfold's research and began treating war wounds with essential oils. Following the war, he published a work entitled *Aromatherapie* which earned him worldwide recognition, after which he began to teach doctors about the healing properties of the oils.

On 3 September, 1928, the face of modern medicine was to change dramatically when Alexander Fleming discovered penicillin. This was, without doubt, a monumental leap forward for modern medicine and one which saved millions of lives, but it also heralded the decline of many natural remedies - at least for a while.

In the mid-twentieth century, a French biochemist called Marguerite Maury took the study of essential oils into the world of cosmetics and it was probably at that point that we have the beginnings of less clarity between what aromatherapy had meant in terms of healing and the somewhat watered down understanding of it as the beauty industry began to expand.

Some fifty to sixty years on, we are once again experiencing a revolution in natural medicines and approaches to healing, with healing aromatics thankfully making a welcome return.

Understanding the Sense of Smell

In order that we are able to perceive smell via the complex procedure of olfaction, the substance being smelled has to meet three requirements:

1. It must be volatile, which means that it is able to become a vapour or gas and therefore have the ability to enter the nostrils.
2. It must be water soluble to enable it to dissolve in mucus and enter the olfactory cells.
3. It must be fat soluble, thereby mimicking the membranes of the olfactory fibres, to enable contact to be made with the tiny olfactory hairs (cilia) in order to provoke a response.

Once these criteria have been met, the beginning of the olfactory process begins with the nose. The nose is commonly referred to as the 'organ of smell', which in part is true, as odour molecules certainly enter the body via the two nasal passages. A series of complex procedures follows so that we are able to perceive smell.

Once the odour molecules enter the nasal cavity, they travel through mucus covered hairs known as *olfactory cilia*. From here they journey on towards the *olfactory epithelium*, where a patch of fifty million receptor cells initiate a nerve impulse that travels from the nasal passage into the brain.

The area of the brain in receipt of the nerve message is called the *olfactory bulb*, which sits at the front of the brain, just above the nasal cavity. Here the nerve message is amplified and travels via the *olfactory tract* into the *limbic system*, so-called because it forms a *limbus* or framework around which the higher parts of the brain are situated.

Within the limbic system, analysis of the odour takes place by two glands known as the *amygdala* and the *hippocampus*, which are the memory and emotional centres of the brain. This explains why inhaling an aroma has the ability to trigger distant or recent memories, or can have an instant effect upon our mood and emotions. If an aroma is new to us, we immediately make a decision as to whether we like it or not based on how we feel, who we are with and what we are doing at that particular moment.,

Once analysis has taken place, the nerve responses travel to the governor or regulator of the brain called the *hypothalamus gland.* The hypothalamus then decides whether to become stimulated in its own right or whether to pass the nerve message on to other glands in the brain, each of which has a specific function. Upon becoming stimulated, the appropriate gland then releases one or a variety of neurochemicals into the bloodstream, which in turn begins to bring about subtle changes in mood and emotion.

The Importance of Olfaction

The importance of smell, or olfaction to give it its correct terminology, plays a bigger part in our lives than we perhaps first realise as the following points illustrate:

1. Smell keeps us safe: It enables us to smell burning in order that we can escape, or detect when a food substance has gone off, therefore preventing us from eating it.
2. Smell identifies territory: Our homes carry a particular smell as do hospitals, the forest or the seaside.
3. On an extremely subtle level, our sense of smell can pick up the pheromones of the opposite sex and as such, subconsciously whispers whether a person is sexually attractive to us.
4. Smell regulates appetite.

5. Smell enables us to perceive flavour. Without the sense of smell we are only able to distinguish between five tastes, namely: Salt, bitter, sweet, sour and savoury.
6. Smell is the only sense that is linked directly to the brain and can, therefore, provide us with an instant reaction, be it comfort or fear.
7. Smell allows humans to distinguish between 10,000 aromas.
8. Smell is capable of changing our moods and emotions due to the release of neurochemicals into the bloodstream.

The Effect of Smell on our Moods, Emotions and Performance

Once an aroma comes into our awareness, regardless of whether we consider it to be pleasant or repulsive, our perception of the immediate world begins to change.

In experiments, two groups of volunteers were shown the same photographs of people who were considered to be 'average looking' and were asked to score them in terms of attractiveness. The first group, who were exposed to a pleasant floral aroma, gave higher attractiveness ratings than the second group, who were in a fragrance free room. No doubt an indicator as to why many of us choose to wear perfumes and aftershaves.

Conversely, the same experiment was carried out using an unpleasant odour as opposed to a pleasant one and the results here were exactly the opposite. The people in the room with the unpleasant odour scored the people in the photographs lower in the attractiveness stakes.

The use of pleasant odours can also encourage us to part with our money, as a Las Vegas casino discovered when infusing a floral fragrance into the air. For during that evening, slot machine gambling increased by forty five percent.

Dr Alan Hirsh, head of the Smell and Taste Research Foundation in Chicago, carried out studies on the power of aroma on shoppers. He placed in two identical rooms, a pair of identical Nike trainers, the first room had a floral aroma infused into the atmosphere, whilst the other remained fragrance free. Eighty four percent of people chose to buy the trainers from the scented room, as they regarded them as being of a better quality and, in addition, said they would be willing to pay on average $10 more for them.

Exposure to certain smells also affects the way in which we absorb and retain information. The use of peppermint oil as a memory stimulant was tested by the Catholic University of America in Washington, where the ability to recall the learning of words increased by fifty percent each time peppermint oil was filtered into the air.

In Japan, the fragrance company Takasago decided to filter various fragrances into their offices at different times of the day in order to enhance different moods as the day wore on. In the morning, lavender oil was infused into the air in order to make people feel relaxed after the rush hour drive and, over a period of time, they noticed that keyboard errors fell by around twenty percent compared to having no aroma filtered into the room. However after lunch they infused lemon oil into the air, to prevent people from feeling sleepy and here keyboard errors fell by a massive fifty four percent, an overwhelmingly successful testament to the powerful sense of smell.

Scent Preferences

When it comes to aromas, we each have our own likes

and dislikes and this is merely to do with our personal memories and emotional responses. It is possible, though, to make certain generalisations. Most people tend to like a smell with which they are familiar, and the overriding aroma that people seem to enjoy in the western hemisphere, regardless of age, sex or health, is vanilla.

The reason for the popularity of this fragrance is difficult to ascertain, however many researchers have attributed it to the fact that it reminds us of our childhood, where hot milky drinks, ice-cream and certain sweets smelled of this fragrance.

In addition to vanilla appealing to our sense of smell, medical research has also shown that it has a marked effect on the reduction of stress and anxiety and has been used with much success during MRI (magnetic resonance imaging) scans in cancer patients. MRI scans are generally known to be stressful; however when *heliotropin*, a vanilla fragrance, is filtered into the scanning machine, patients recorded anxiety levels reduce by up to sixty three percent.

Throughout the world as a whole, vanilla is not the preferred aroma. The cattle raising Dassanetch people of Ethiopia love nothing more than the scent of their cows. So revered is this aroma and such is the association with status and fertility, that the men wash their hands in the cattle urine and smear the manure over their bodies, whilst the women rub the butter into their breasts to make themselves more attractive to their men folk.

In Mali, the Dogon people prefer the scent of fried onions, which is massaged into the skin before going out with a loved one or prospective suitor.

Perhaps the most complex blending of aromas is found in Arabic countries, where women use a variety of scents with which to perfume different parts of their bodies.

When my husband and I were in Saudi Arabia, we spent an evening with our hosts and their families, albeit men and women were segregated and ate in different parts of the house.

After the meal, my hostess brought out a beautifully carved box, which when opened revealed a variety of attractive bottles. Each bottle contained a different perfume with which to anoint a particular part of the body and included: rose, saffron, sandalwood, jasmine and narcissus.

Finally a fragrant smoking incense burner was brought into the room containing *Oudh*, a type of aloe wood with which we scented our a*bayas* (long black robes).

It was explained to me that through the sharing of beautiful aromas, we now had an unbreakable emotional bond. This ritual marked the end of the visit and I left with an overall sense of well-being.

Smell and Sexual Attraction

It has long been recognised that women in particular are highly sensitive to male pheromones, particularly around the time of ovulation. This has led many men to believe that the odour of their natural sweat is attractive to females, however all male pheromones are not born equal.

The male pheromone *androstenol* is produced from fresh male sweat which females tend to find very attractive. The pheromone *androstenone*, however, is certainly not an attractor, as this is the scent produced from male sweat that has been exposed to oxygen and is often regarded as 'highly unpleasant' by females.

Back in 1991, a commercial company carried out

research on androstenone. They scented a variety of overdue invoices and bills with the pheromone and concluded (this has not been independently verified) that seventeen percent more people (both men and women) paid their bills, as they perceived the bills to be threatening.

On the other side of the coin, many women believe that the use of perceived 'sexy' perfumes, containing musk aromas, will attract men, but a woman's sensitivity to musk is 1,000 times greater than a man's and he will probably only feel aroused because of the effect the scent has on her, rather than the direct effect it has on him.

Up until the late eighteenth century, the most popular perfumes were heavy powerful aromas derived from animals such as musk, civet and ambergris, which were used, according to the psychologist Havelock Ellis, not to mask a woman's natural smell but rather to enhance it.

Around this time, however, partly due to advances in sanitation, bodily hygiene, the new moralistic temperance movement and 'political correctness', more delicate aromas became the order of the day and strong perfumes began to cast doubt on the wearer's cleanliness.

In contrast, men throughout the ages have felt less need to advertise their masculinity with scented potions.

Here the thirteenth century Arab poet (one of the major Persian poets of the 13th century Medieval period) Sheykh Moslehoddi Sadi tells us:

'*Essence of roses, fragrant aloes, paint, perfume and lust: All these are ornaments of women. Take a man; and his testicles are a sufficient ornaments.*'

Men are not totally immune to being influenced by aromas, for some reports have suggested that the fragrance of cinnamon is said to help with erectile dysfunction. The Smell and Taste Research Foundation in Chicago have added pumpkin pie, liquorice, doughnuts, Coca-Cola and lavender to this list, whilst adding the disclaimer that many other factors also have to be taken into account such as, how attractive a man finds his partner and how many times they have had sex during the previous month.

Technology today allows the accurate analysis and synthetic production of thousands of different smells. New fragrances for men include; the aroma of a New York tobacconist's shop, essence of racing car and the scent of the financial newspapers. This may be fine in concept, but the question remains as to whether women will find these aromas sexually attractive.

Sensitivity to Smell

We all respond differently to aromas according to our sex, age and health. Women have been proven to have a far more sensitive sense of smell than men, leading some researchers to claim that this superior olfactory ability of females is evident even in newborn babies. It is because of this heightened sensitivity that women are far more likely to suffer from *cacosmia*, the name given to feeling ill from certain environmental chemicals such as paint, household cleaners and perfume.

The sense of smell, as we have seen, develops between eleven to fifteen weeks in the womb and is therefore present at birth. Experiments have shown that a newborn baby is able to locate its mother's nipple by smell alone. During these experiments, one breast of each mother was washed immediately after birth and the baby placed between the breasts. Twenty two babies out of thirty selected the unwashed breast to feed from.

The sense of smell gradually increases in children until they reach the age of eight, at which point it plateaus out, whilst between the ages of twenty and eighty it begins to decrease, a fact determined by a person's mental and physical health.

The Importance of Electronic Noses

During the last twenty-five years, the importance of the sense of smell has slowly become recognised, leading to the first prototype electronic nose being produced during the 1980s by The Institute of Olfactory Research at Warwick University. Commercial versions of the 'Warwick nose' are now sold throughout the world to perfumers and customs people alike.

Perhaps more importantly, researchers at Warwick are looking into the use of electronic noses in order to be able to detect illness by smelling a patient's breath. Research has even progressed as far as looking at installing a minute electronic nose into a phone receiver so that a patient can breathe into it and await a diagnosis. In a similar way breath analysis can be used in identifying different stages of a woman's menstrual cycle which could ultimately benefit both fertility and birth control.

This idea of 'sniffing out disease' however is far from new as Avicenna, way back in 1000AD, diagnosed certain illnesses by sniffing the aroma of a patient's urine, whilst Hippocrates was an adept at smelling a patient's body odour as an effective means of identifying their ailments.

Electronic noses are no more sensitive to smells than the human nose, but where they win over is in the fact that they do not get bored with constantly smelling the same odours, nor do they become desensitised. If the smell is unpleasant then the electronic nose does not feel sick, nor does it fluctuate in its opinion due to hormonal changes or mood.

Essential Oils in Healing

One of the most effective ways of benefiting from aromatic healing today is through the use of essential oils. Essential oils are present in many varieties of flowers, grasses, herbs, trees, and fruit and are to be found in many different parts of a plant, namely; petals, leaves, bark, wood, roots, entire aerial, plant and fruit peel, each of which has its own particular way of storing oil from glandular cells or hairs to oil resin canals and reservoirs.

The term 'aromatherapy', or 'aromatherapie' as it was originally known, was coined back in the 1920s by the French chemist Rene Maurice Gattefosse to describe the practice of using essential oils in the healing of both mind and emotions.

In the interim period, the art and science of aromatherapy has blossomed and is now offered as an 'aromatherapy massage treatment' by spas, beauty salons and complementary health clinics.

The former two, although providing undeniably relaxing treatments, will often use pre blended oils and may offer a choice of either a 'relaxing' or 'uplifting' blend. This means that very little essential oil knowledge is actually applied by the therapist with regards to meeting the individual needs of the client. Conversely, however, in a complementary health clinic, the likelihood of finding a properly qualified aromatherapist who will tailor-make an oil blend based on the client's needs is much higher.

Due to the ability of essential oils to bring about profound effects on our moods and emotions, we can all benefit from burning oils around the home in order to enhance our psychological well-being.

Table 1.7, after this, provides examples of specific essential oils and is based on research by Robert Tisserand.

For perfuming a room, place a little water on an incense burner and add a MAXIMUM of 6 drops of essential oil. Please note that the contraindications listed ONLY apply to use by inhalation. Topical use is far more complex. If you are unsure, please consult a qualified aromatherapist.

Essential Oil	Gland(s) triggered and neuro-chemical(s) secreted	Emotional & psychological effects, energy field impact & contraindications
Lemon *(Citrus limonum)*	Amygdala/ Hippocampus Various	Lemon refreshes, enlivens and helps to clarify the thought processes. It works on the 2nd and 6th layers of the auric field and the crown chakra. It releases creative and spiritual energy blocks.
Peppermint *(Mentha piperita)*	Amygdala/ Hippocampus Various	Peppermint cools anger and hysteria. Excellent for mental fatigue, enhancing memory and lifting depressive states. Peppermint works on the 6th layer of the aura and the throat and brow chakras to encourage freedom of thought. A strong aroma; with overuse leading to irritation of the sensitive membranes of the eyes and nose.
Geranium *(Pelargonium graveolens)*	Hypothalamus Various	Geranium acts as a stress reliever and balancer for the mind and nervous system, easing both anxious and

		depressive states. Geranium works on the 2nd and 4th layers of the aura and balances the sacral and heart chakras. It encourages harmony between sexuality, spirituality and the emotions.
Frankincense *(Boswellia carteri)*	Hypothalamus Various	Frankincense has been revered for thousands of years for its ability to expand the consciousness and accelerate the meditative state. It regulates, calms and balances. Frankincense works on the 1st, 6th and 7th layers of the aura, the solar plexus and crown chakras. It releases ties to things which no longer serve us, allowing us to grow spiritually.
Clary Sage *(Salvia sclarea)*	Thalamus Enkephalins	Clary Sage soothes nervous tension, a racing mind and panic. It brings feelings of euphoria and well-being, allowing us to see things in perspective. Clary sage works on the 3rd and 5th layers of the aura and balances the sacral and brow chakras, assisting us with acceptance and clarity. A strong oil which may affect the reactions. Avoid use if driving or consuming alcohol.
Rose Otto	Thalamus	Rose Otto soothes the emotions, lifts the heart,

(Rosa damascena)	Enkephalins	eases stress and brings positive feelings. It is particularly indicated for grief. Rose resonates with the 2nd, 3rd and 4th layers of the aura and balances the sacral and heart chakras. It awakens sexuality, the senses, our love for others and ourselves.
Patchouli *(Pogostemon patchouli)*	Pituitary Endorphins	Patchouli allows the mind to be more objective. Its earthy aroma is both grounding and sensual and is a renowned aphrodisiac. Patchouli works on the 1st 3rd and 4th layers of the aura and with the base and sacral chakras. It resonates with the frequency of wants and desires although not necessarily in a material sense. A powerful aroma; it is sedative in low doses and stimulating in high doses.
Ylang Ylang *(Cananga Odorata)*	Pituitary Endorphins	Ylang Ylang eases both anxious and depressive states. It relaxes the nervous system, soothing feelings of anger, anxiety, shock, panic and fear, whilst bringing feelings of joy and affection. Ylang Ylang works on the 5th layer of the aura, the sacral and brow chakras to bring determination and truth to the fore when the nerve is faltering.
Chamomile (Roman)	Raphe Nucleus	Chamomile soothes the mind and encourages sleep.

(Anthemis nobilis)	Serotonin	It is particularly good for fractious children. Chamomile works on the 3rd layer of the aura, bringing control to our mental energies. It balances the throat and brow chakras, helping us to speak calmly but firmly.
Lavender *(Lavendula Officinalis)*	Raphe Nucleus Serotonin	It has a positive effect on the mind and emotions encouraging peaceful sleep. It relieves anger and eases stressful states due to its balancing effect on the central nervous system. Lavender works across the spectrum of the human energy field, healing and balancing on all levels. It can cause feelings of drowsiness.

Table 1.7

Dedication

For me, the sense of smell reminds me of my spiritual connection and is the sense through which I am able to access a different state of consciousness.

To enter a sacred space and be greeted by the aroma of frankincense can instantly transport me to higher planes. The smell of the forest on a hot summer's day lets me know that I am home; the smell of the sea tells me that I am standing on the edge of the land with only adventure before me, whilst aromatic smoke has the power to transport and transform ... carrying my dreams to the realms of the gods.

The following dedication to the goddess is an example of how we can express our appreciation for our sense of smell. Light a white or purple candle, symbolic of the crown centre and spiritual connectedness, burn some incense or essential oils and chant the following dedication:

> *Lady Goddess, gift bearer of the senses,*
> *I appreciate and honour my sense of smell.*
> *I give thanks that through smell I am able to enjoy the fragrance of nature,*
> *I give thanks that through smell my loved ones and I are kept from danger,*
> *I give thanks that through smell I am able to both give and receive healing.*
> *Please accept this fragrant offering as a token of my gratitude.*

Let the candle burn right down if possible. It may be a generous gesture to give something aromatic to a friend or loved one, such as incense or perfume.

Conclusion

Our sense of smell is a precious gift that evokes memories, keeps us safe and transports us to other times and places. It has the ability to heal emotional turmoil, soothe troubled minds and lift the spirit, whilst also healing ailments of a more physical nature.

By taking time to fragrance our homes with a few drops of well chosen essential oils, we are able to bring about subtle changes in our moods and emotions, thereby having the ability to ultimately change our consciousness.

Mrs Darley Tale: The Ritual

'I love your cottage,' I said to Mrs Darley as we sat beside her fire one frosty January evening, 'it's so cosy and welcoming.'

'Well, that's very kind of you to say so, my dear, but you make it sound as though yours isn't.'

'No … well yes … oh, I don't know, no matter how many times I change the décor and move the furniture around it never seems … well, right somehow. It's almost as though it's sad. Does that sound silly?'

Mrs Darley shook her head. 'No it doesn't sound silly at all, and, in fact, I think you're probably picking up on the energy vibrations of the people who lived there before. You see, my dear, your cottage wasn't a very happy place.'

'What do you mean, not happy?' I said.

'It was full of infidelities, recriminations, arguments and neglect.'

'In what way?' I asked, a rush of anxiety beginning to make itself felt in the pit of my stomach.

'It matters little now, my dear. Thankfully those times are over.'

'I had no idea,' I said, 'I never met the people who owned it, as the estate agent showed me around and yet, as I mentioned, I've never been able to get it feeling quite right.

'May I make a suggestion?' Mrs Darley asked.

I nodded. 'Please do.'

'Perhaps you would like to participate in a purification ritual to cleanse your cottage of any negative energies; a type of house healing you might say?'

'Oh yes,' I said, 'yes I would; that would be very welcome.'

'Then we will arrange the ritual for Sunday evening, the night of the first new moon in February, the month of purification.'

'Sounds good to me,' I said, 'is there anything I need

to do or get?'

Mrs Darley shook her head. 'No, I will bring what is necessary, all I would ask is that you clean the cottage from top to bottom beforehand and then take a purification bath, using an essential oil blend that I will prepare for you.

'I can do that.'

'Then I will see you on Sunday, my dear,' said Mrs Darley.

My cleaning duties began bright and early on Sunday morning and, as I took my duster out into the porch, I noticed a small package lying on the floor. I opened it up to find a small muslin bag secured at the top by a looped piece of thread. The bag contained what felt like plant material and gave off quite an earthy aroma. I read the accompanying note which read:

This is for your purification bath. Hang it over the tap and let it float in the water. Whilst you're in the bath, visualize yourself bathed in a white light. See you about 7pm. Mrs D.

With the housework complete, I took my purification bath and although I found the visualization of the white light difficult to maintain, I rose from the bath feeling quite refreshed. However, as 7pm approached, I began to feel increasingly nervous and was relieved when Mrs Darley arrived to end my anticipation.

'Hello, dear,' she said as she swept into the room with a bag and a beautiful bunch of white flowers. 'Did you get my note and bath potion?'

I nodded. 'Yes, I've cleansed both the house and myself.'

'Good,' she smiled. 'Now then, do you think we could

move that little table over to this side of the room, just in front of the fire?'

With the table in position, Mrs Darley covered it with a white cloth and began to place upon it the flowers, a white candle and several other items from her bag, the purpose of which was a mystery to me.

I continued to watch however, as she poured water from a tiny flask into a silver bowl, to which she added a pinch of salt. This was followed by the lighting of what I later learned was a charcoal block, carefully secreted within an incense burner.

'There now,' she said, 'I think we're almost ready to begin.'

I nodded, forcing a smile.

'Oh, my dear,' said Mrs Darley, 'there's no need to look so worried. This is a simple cleansing ritual; cottage magick. All I would ask you to do is to try and visualize whatever I suggest.'

'I wasn't very good at it earlier,' I said, 'I found it difficult to see the white light when taking my bath.'

'Well, now is the time to try again,' Mrs Darley smiled, 'just do it as best you can, for then your energies will add to mine and the magick will be more powerful. Come!'

With this she took my hand and we stood before the little table, while she spoke the following words:

'Our task tonight is the cleansing and purification of this cottage, to drive dark, harmful and negative energies away and bring those of love light and positivity in their place. May those who watch over us add their power to our actions.'

Mrs Darley then took two strange looking bundles of tied

plant material from the table and lit them in the flames of the wood burning stove.

'Here you are, dear,' she said blowing out the flames and handing me one of the smouldering bundles, 'it's a white sage smudge stick and has been used in the Native American Indian tradition for centuries for the purpose of cleansing and purification. Let's begin upstairs.'

We went first of all into the bathroom, where Mrs Darley indicated that I should follow her in walking 'widdershins'[2], which she later explained was anti-clockwise around the room.

The smouldering bundles were now emitting quite a pungent earthy aroma, which I quite enjoyed and as we came round to the window she opened it and said, 'Let the four winds take all dark, harmful and negative energies from this place.'

Our actions, my visualizations and Mrs Darley's words were repeated in every room until we found ourselves once more in the lounge before the little table. Here she sprinkled something onto the now grey charcoal block, which instantly transformed into the most beautiful spirals of aromatic smoke.

'Frankincense,' she said as she paused to inhale the fragrance which seemed to momentarily transport her elsewhere, 'healer of souls. Now, my dear, you take this,' she said as she handed me the bowl of smoking incense, 'and I will bring the salted water.'

Once again we went into the bathroom, but this time Mrs Darley began by closing the window, before dipping her finger into the bowl of salted water and drawing what

---

[2] Sometimes withershins, widershins or widderschynnes - means to take a course opposite the apparent motion of the sun, to go counterclockwise.

I now know was an invoking pentagram on the glass pane.
'With the elements of water and earth, I cleanse and purify this room, may love, light and positivity fill this space.'

She then handed the bowl to me, exchanging it for the bowl of smouldering incense and once again drew a pentagram on the window pane through the mist of fragrant smoke.

'With the elements of fire and air, I cleanse and purify this room, may love, light and positivity fill this space.'

She repeated her actions as she closed the bathroom door and then followed the same pattern throughout the cottage until we once again found ourselves back in the lounge and, taking my hand, she said:

'To the ancients who have added their power to our intent we honour and thank you and ask that this house be filled with the healing energies of love, joy and happiness.'

At this point she squeezed my hand before releasing it, 'There, my dear,' she said, 'our magick is done.'

Pheromones
Intoxicating, heady; sense and senses depart.
Drunk, drugged to the point of delicious delirium.
Priorities alter; change of life layout ahead.
Familiarity closes her door; another world awaits.
Bewitched or blessed; I care little.
Captivated or cursed; it matters not.

Metaphorical wings lift my spirit.
Mediocrity tumbles from my dictionary.

I have no answer, no rationale.
Words are mere inadequacies,
Explanations; defy understanding,
Pheromones; lie beyond detection.

Chapter 6

The Sense of Taste

The Taste of Lust
The day is born sweet.
Sugared promises
Feed my mind. I wait.

You come.

My tongue rejoices.
Rivers of salted sweat
Feed my taste buds.

You come.

It is almost time.
The day is soured.
You are already hers.

You go

Bitterness descends
As a mist veiled in Time.
My world grows dark.

I am alone.

Mrs Darley Tale: Kneading the Dough

'Goodness me, you're home early,' said Mrs Darley as I walked past her cottage on my way round from the car, 'is everything alright?'

I smiled at her. 'Yes, everything's fine. Well, I say fine, we've had a bomb scare at work this morning.'

'Oh, dear,' said Mrs Darley, 'is everyone alright?'

'Yes. It was just a hoax, but the police took over our office so I said I'd work from home for the rest of the day. Oooo!' I said instantly stopping to sniff the air, 'what's that wonderful smell coming from your cottage? Because whatever it is, it's making me feel quite hungry.'

'It's homemade herb bread,' Mrs Darley replied. 'Phyllis and I are making a few loaves for Lucy's harvest festival at school. Look, if you'd like a couple of hours break before going back to your laptop, perhaps you'd like to join us? We're just about to make brown beer bread and you'd be doing us both a favour if you'd help out with the kneading. Payment for your services comes by way of a slice of bread and a wedge of cheese.'

'Sounds good to me,' I said, 'I'll be round in five minutes.'

I duly arrived and was immediately swept into a hive of industry in Mrs Darley's tiny kitchen, with Phyllis measuring, Mrs Darley mixing and me kneading.

'Oh I must do this more often,' I said, 'I feel as though I'm getting rid of all my pent up feelings with this kneading.'

'What you must remember, my dear,' said Mrs Darley watching me pound the dough into the floured board, 'is that whenever you make something, you take on the role of the creator and as such, you put a little of your energy into whatever it is. It is important therefore to infuse your kneading with positive thoughts.'

'Oh, dear,' I laughed, 'did I look as though I was punching someone?'

'Gently pummelling perhaps,' she smiled. 'You see, this bread will be used after the service to provide a harvest supper for the elderly of the Parish and it's important that it is full of nourishment and good energies.'

'Point taken,' I said, making a concerted effort to not only knead the dough more gently, but also move my thoughts away from work and into the task in hand.

When at last the beer dough had been set aside for proving, we all filtered into the lounge with a wedge of herb bread, still warm from an earlier batch of baking and a selection of delicious cheeses.

'This is so good,' I said as I helped myself to a second wedge of bread.

'Food made with love and shared amongst friends always tastes better than that which is commercially produced and eaten alone. The first Hermetic principle states that the creator always leaves a spark of his or her Divine energy within everything that is, and making bread is no different.'

'That makes sense,' I said, 'but what is a *Hermetic principle*?'

'Ah,' said Mrs Darley, 'now there's a question. How long do you have, my dear?'

Introducing the Sense of Taste

The sense of taste, or 'gustation' to give it its more formal title, is the third of our senses to develop and is present at around fourteen weeks in the womb. At birth, a baby's taste buds are very well developed, due to being exposed to the varied diet of the mother whilst in the womb.

If we are lucky, we form an emotional bond with our mothers through being breast fed and this emotional connection to food is something that stays with us throughout life, often being reflected in the language we choose to describe our feelings.

We tend to use sweetness to describe the good things in our lives such as 'she was a sweetheart' or 'the sweet smell of success'.

However, our language pattern changes when someone says something to us that hurts our feelings. On occasions such as these we may say that 'it was hard to swallow', an 'acidic comment', or that it 'left a bad taste in the mouth'. In fact the word 'disgust' derives from the word gustation which literally translated means 'to leave a bad taste'.

Gustation refers to our ability to differentiate between the tastes of various substances including: food and certain minerals and poisons. Yet for all the pleasure we derive from tasting our food, this sense is the poor relation in comparison with others.

As a stand alone sense, taste can offer us very little and has, until recently in the Western world, only been thought to provide us with the experience of four tastes:

- Sweet
- Sour
- Salt
- Bitter

The concept of these basic tastes can be traced back to Aristotle, who considered just sweet and bitter to be the basics, but that the following were elaborations:

- Succulent

- Salt
- Pungent
- Harsh
- Puckery (bitter or astringent, causing the mouth to pucker)
- Sour

In eastern culture, other tastes have been acknowledged for thousands of years and in ancient Chinese manuscripts five tastes are mentioned which include:

- Sweet
- Sour
- Salt
- Bitter
- Savouriness or '*Umami*' in Japanese e.g. monosodium glutamate

The latter, has now been accepted by scientists in the west and since the year 2002, savoury has been accepted as a fifth taste.

In the ancient Indian healing modality of Ayurveda, written texts refer to six tastes:

- Sweet
- Sour
- Salt
- Bitter
- Hot / Pungent / Piquant (the sensation associated with chilli peppers)
- Astringent or dry (Kasaava in Sanskrit)

More recently, psychophysicists and neuroscientists have

suggested other taste categories which include:

- Fatty Acids e.g. linoleic acid
- Metallic (not from food, but from blood in the mouth)

It is, however, only when taste has the added help of the sense of smell that we are able to experience real flavour, which is why, when we have a cold and our nasal passages become blocked, we are unable to taste our food.

This chapter sets out to explore not only the sense of taste in its strictest form, but also investigates the reasons behind our eating habits and how we can achieve good health through a well balanced diet.

Understanding the Sense of Taste

For all the research carried out on our sense of taste, the actual mechanics are still somewhat of a mystery to us. What we do know however is that taste is a sensory function of the central nervous system and that there are approximately 9,000 minute barrel shaped taste buds or *gustatory calyculi*, located mainly on the upper surface of the tongue.

In addition, there are further taste buds in the throat, the roof of the mouth and the soft palate. The tip of each taste bud carries a group of between fifteen to twenty taste receptors, which are linked to nerve fibres whose task is to carry taste impulses to the brain.

These taste receptors have a very short life and are replaced every seven days and as we grow older, the amount of taste buds decrease, which explains why older people tend to use more salt and sugar in order to be able to taste their food.

Although the majority of literature available on taste states that different parts of the tongue are receptive to different tastes, for example the tip of the tongue is sensitive to sweet foods, whilst further back it is able to detect bitter tastes, this is a misconception due to the mistranslation of a German text early in the twentieth century.

In actual fact, all taste sensations arise in all regions of the oral cavity. What we now know, though, is that the receptors for sour and salty tastes are detected by 'ion channels', whilst the receptors for sweet, bitter and savoury are detected by 'G protein coupled receptors'.

It appears that when molecules of food come into contact with the tongue they form a bond with the molecular structure of the taste cell, which in turn excites the nerve fibre and gives rise to a nerve impulse. The central nervous system relays these messages to the brain, which identifies the taste and associates it with a particular food.

The actual experience of flavour, then again, is far more complex and involves other senses and qualities. Our eyes tell the brain what to expect, the texture of the food is detected by mechanoreceptors, whilst the temperature of the food is detected by thermoreceptors.

However, it is the sense of smell that is probably the most important contributor to our overall enjoyment of food, for when the smell of food, which is detected by the olfactory epithelium, is combined with taste, we are able to experience true flavour, rather than simple basic tastes.

There are many factors which can affect the way we perceive food to taste:

- Age
- Visual impairment

- Hormonal disorders
- Oral temperature
- Consumption of some drugs
- Neurological disorders
- Anosmia (inability to smell)
- Blocked nasal passages
- Zinc deficiency
- Ageusia (complete loss of taste)
- Dysgeusia (persistent abnormal taste)

Exploring Taste

Savoury tastes like salt and sweet are referred to as 'appetitive', whilst bitter and sour tastes are referred to as 'aversive'. The appetitive tastes are the ones that drive us towards essential nutrients, whilst the aversive alert us to potentially harmful substances such as poisons, although not all bitter or sour foods are poisonous.

Adults often acquire a taste for foods that combine appetitive and aversive tastes, including; coffee with cream or sugar, olives with cheese, or sweet and sour dishes in Chinese cooking.

Bitterness:

Bitterness is the most sensitive of the tastes and is often perceived to be rather unpleasant or sharp, although we do, as a nation, tend to consume rather a large amount of foods that have a bitter taste:

- Coffee
- Marmalade
- Olives
- Bitter beer
- Citrus peel

- Brassicacaea family (sprouts, cauliflower)
- Lemons
- Quinine (tonic water)

Many poisonous plants are bitter in taste and therefore our ability to detect bitterness has the potential to keep us safe from ingesting foods that have not been tried and tested.

Sour

Sourness is the taste that detects acidity and the sourness of a substance is rated relative to dilute hydrochloric acid. Hydrogen ion channels are responsible for detecting sourness, which is formed from a combination of acids and water. The most common sour food groups include:

- Lemon
- Orange
- Wine
- Spoiled milk
- Vinegar
- Sour sweets containing citric acid (lemon drops)

Salt

Salt is a taste produced by the presence of sodium ions, although other ions of the alkali metals group also taste salty such as lithium and potassium.

Sweet

Sweetness is one of the tastes considered to be pleasant and is produced, in the main, by the presence of sugars and proteins. At least two variants of the sweetness receptors in the mouth need to be activated before the brain is able to register sweetness.

Savouriness (Umami)

Savouriness is used to describe tastes produced by amino acids such as glutamate and is commonly found in fermented and aged foods. It is often described as meaty, or rich. Savoury tastes can be found in:

- Beef / Lamb
- Parmesan cheese
- Roquefort cheese
- Soy sauce
- Fish sauce
- Monosodium glutamate

The tongue is also capable of feeling other sensations that are not generally classified as one of the five basic tastes and these are largely detected by the somatosensory system.

These can include the sensations of fattiness from greasy food, dryness from tea, red wine or rhubarb, metallicness from the presence of blood in the mouth and prickliness or hotness from chilli peppers, ginger or horseradish.

Other factors in the Taste Experience

Temperature is an essential element of the human taste experience, part of which comes from conditioning at an early age as to the preferred heat that we enjoy certain food and drink. Some foods, though, can produce perceived heat effects. A mint sweet made with *crystalline sorbitol* produces a positive heat solution, therefore providing a cooling effect to the tongue, whilst a mint sweet containing *amorphous sorbitol* produces a negative heat solution and causes a warm sensation in the mouth.

Many foods are so strong that they are likely to leave an aftertaste in the mouth, which may be either pleasant or decidedly unpleasant. Alcohol, spicy foods and aspartame, the artificial sweetener, are all capable of this.

Developing an 'acquired taste' is something that manifests when we are exposed to a strong smelling or flavoured food type over a period of time.

When visiting Kuala Lumpar in Malaysia, my husband and I were introduced to their prized delicacy, the durian fruit.

One morning, a doctor, who was attending our course, gave me a Tupperware box, wrapped in several plastic bags, explaining that it was a durian fruit which he hoped I would enjoy. He warned me, however, not to open it until I was in the open air and far away from anyone else as it was an offence to eat it in an enclosed public place due to the overpowering smell. I later told the course organiser of my gift who, with a wry smile suggested that we should drive down to the basement of the car park where we could try it, well away from anyone else. I was intrigued, but as I began to unwrap it, anxiety surpassed the intrigue.

As soon as the first plastic bag was taken away, the smell began to escape from the Tupperware box and I could feel my stomach begin to roll. To my western senses this was an assault of the highest order. It was a smell that was quite indescribable. However, in order to attempt a description, I would have to say that it was a combination of drains and rubbish bins on a very hot day. Eventually I reached the fruit itself and was challenged to eat a piece, but as I picked it up my fingers went right through it just as though it was rotten. Undeterred however, I took a deep breath and placed it in my mouth. I am ashamed to say that my taste experience was extremely limited, for no sooner it was in my mouth it came out again into a waiting tissue. My friend laughed and said perhaps now I would understand how the Malaysians felt about blue cheese!

The History behind our Food Choices

Many of our food choices, although we are unlikely to be aware of the fact, are deeply rooted in our cultural history. Due to our strategic geographical location and the fact that we have always been a magnet for invaders, our cuisine has gradually evolved as an eclectic mix of food styles.

Early Celtic agriculture ensured that we always had a variety of grain in our diet in addition to meat products acquired through hunting. The Roman invasion maximised the rich British soil to produce high quality crops and advanced animal breeding techniques. The later Anglo Saxons introduced savoury herbs and stewed meat dishes to the British diet, whilst the Vikings brought traditional Nordic fish dishes. The Norman Conquest introduced eastern spices and sugar to these shores. The later building of the British Empire ensured that more exotic influences came our way in the form of tea and curry spices from India.

During the Second World War, however, food supplies to Britain were in sharp decline, resulting in our culinary skills becoming somewhat diminished and, as a result, we became a nation of stews, pies, breads, cakes, stodgy puddings and fish and chips.

It was not until the 1980s that British cuisine picked itself up from the gutter and began to look for a new direction, resurrecting largely forgotten dishes such as game, shell fish and offal, whilst also embracing the more exotic dishes of India, China and the Mediterranean. This has resulted in a reduction of potato consumption in favour of pasta and rice and, a fall in the amount of animal fats used, in favour of vegetable oils.

Some favourites still hold strong, such as roast beef and Yorkshire pudding, the great British fried breakfast, bangers and mash, bubble and squeak and seaside fish and chips. Many dishes which were once classified as regional specialities such as black pudding, Cornish pasties, clotted cream, haggis, Welsh rarebit, Eccles cakes, Irish stew, and a variety of regional cheeses, are now revered not only as national dishes, but are also served, albeit with a twist, in many high end restaurants.

Today British cuisine is some of the most varied and highly respected in the world, having shrugged off our unglamorous reputation of being the poor relation of culinary delights.

Food Choices and Preferences

The reasons for our food choices are almost as varied as the types of food available and can be dependant not only upon our own personal taste, but also a myriad of external influences including:

- Health
- Emotional and psychological disorders which can manifest in eating disorders
- Religion
- Culture
- Price
- Ethical choices

Each of these ultimately has the power to affect us on a spiritual, psychological, emotional and physical level.

Eating for Health

If we decided to eat with our eyes we would probably all be much healthier, for we would, no doubt, be attracted to the colourful array of fruit and vegetables that are always available. Sadly, however, although we know what we should be eating, many of us tend to opt for products that instantly satisfy our hunger, such as sugary, starchy or fatty foods. Over time we become addicted to these choices that both expand our waistline and contribute to poor health.

Basic Food Groups

In order to eat healthily, our diet should contain a combination of the four basic food types and although it is beyond the remit of this book to discuss specific dietary requirements and daily allowances, an overview of these food types are discussed below.

Carbohydrates

Carbohydrates comprise of two distinct types, viz: simple and complex, although both are capable of providing the body with energy and warmth.

Simple carbohydrates contain mainly simple sugars which begin the digestion process as soon as they are taken into the mouth. They very quickly enter the bloodstream where they give an instant boost of energy but play havoc with blood sugar levels. Any excess sugar is stored in the liver and muscles for future energy, but a constant build up of excess sugar is stored as fat. Many simple carbohydrates are packed with 'empty calories' such as sugary sweets and processed foods, whilst others have additional nutritional benefits such as some fruits, honey and dairy; however daily intake should be limited. Simple carbohydrates include:

- Boiled sweets
- Cakes / pastries
- Tinned fruit
- White bread
- Honey
- Some Fruits

Complex carbohydrates are preferable in the diet as they contain a combination of sugars, starch, fibre, vitamins and minerals. These are harder to digest and provide a storehouse of slow release energy, ensuring blood sugar levels are kept on an even keel. Complex carbohydrates include:

- Whole grains
- Wholemeal Bread
- Wholegrain Pasta
- Brown rice
- Potatoes
- Sweet potatoes
- Parsnips
- Sweet corn
- Bananas

Proteins

Protein helps the body to grow and repair. It plays an essential role in maintaining all bodily processes such as muscle contraction, immune protection, transmission of nerve impulses and support of skin and bones. If carbohydrate or fat intake is too low, the body can metabolise protein for use as energy. If too much protein is consumed and not metabolised, it is stored as fat. There are two types of protein, viz: complete and incomplete.

Animal derived foods are a major source of complete proteins as they contain all the essential amino acids in the proportions that the body needs.

The downside to this is that because these foods comprise of full fat dairy products or fatty meat, the risk of life threatening illnesses increase including; stroke, cancers and heart disease. White meats and poultry such as chicken and lean pork can dramatically reduce the amount of fat consumption, whilst eggs are one of the most complete forms of protein known at the present time.

Complete proteins include:

- Meat / Poultry / Game
- Fish
- Cheese
- Milk
- Yoghurt
- Eggs

Plant foods are unable to contribute all the essential amino acids needed in a healthy diet and are, therefore, referred to as incomplete amino acids. For vegetarians, it is essential to know which incomplete foods contain which amino acids in order that the body receives all that it needs. Incomplete proteins include:

- Beans
- Nuts and Seeds
- Pulses
- Rice
- Oats
- Pasta

- Cereals
- Soya products
- Quorn
- Mushroom

Fats

Fatty acids provide the most concentrated source of calories. Fats are essential for healthy childhood development as they regulate the body's metabolism, provide warmth and energy, form a protective layer of fat around the heart and kidneys, make food tasty and help the body to store fat soluble vitamins such as A, D, E and K. Lack of fat leads to a lack of energy, feeling cold, loss of weight and vitamin deficiencies. Fats fall into two categories, viz: saturated and unsaturated.

Saturated fats tend to be solid at room temperature and are thought to contribute to high cholesterol levels, which can lead to heart attack, stroke and some cancers. Saturated fats include:

- Butter / margarine
- Hard Cheese
- Coconut oil
- Fatty meat
- Full cream milk
- Cream
- Lard and suet

Unsaturated fats are often referred to as the 'good fats', which the body needs to provide the functions outlined above. These are broken down into two categories, viz: monosaturated and polyunsaturated.

Monosaturated fats provide omega 9, which is thought to reduce the risk of heart disease, stokes and cancers.

Food sources include:

- Olive oil
- Nut oils
- Nuts
- Seeds
- Avocados

Polyunsaturated fats provide omega 3, which helps with the development of the brain and eyes, reduces inflammation and assists in the treatment of heart disease and arthritis. Food sources include:

- Oily fish
- Linseed oil
- Rapeseed oil
- Walnuts
- Soya beans

Polyunsaturated fats also provide Omega 6, which contributes to cell makeup and helps to maintain a strong immune system. Food sources include:

- Almonds
- Evening primrose oil
- Sunflower oil

Fibre

The role of fibre in stimulating bowel function has been recognised since ancient times and its virtues are extolled in the Bible, where we are told that when Daniel ate only vegetables and drank water for ten days, he was healthier than the young men who ate rich food and drank wine at the King's table.

In the 1970s, Drs Burkitt and Trowell discovered that fibre plays an important role in the prevention of certain diseases including: IBS, cancers of the digestive tract, colitis, diabetes, constipation, haemorrhoids and raised cholesterol. There are two types of fibre, viz: insoluble and soluble:

Insoluble fibre absorbs water, therefore making faeces easier to pass. It also ferments in the large intestine which nourishes the intestinal wall and helps to fill us up, thereby preventing us from eating more than we need. Food sources include:

- Wholegrain bread
- Brown rice
- Wholegrain Cereals
- Fruit
- Vegetables
- Nuts and seeds
- Grains

Soluble fibre is partially digestible and breaks down in the digestive tract to form fatty acids which, when absorbed into the blood stream, help to control cholesterol. Fibre has the ability to bind simple sugars to it therefore ensuring they take longer to digest and reducing cases of diabetes and hyperglycaemia. Food sources include:

- Oats
- Beans
- Pulses
- Peas

- Carrots
- Parsnips
- Potatoes

Vitamins

In addition to the basic food types, it is also necessary to have sufficient vitamins and minerals in our diet in order to maintain good health.

Vitamins are chemical compounds that occur in both plant and animal foods and have shown to be essential for life.

The word vitamin was given to these compounds by Dr Casimir Funk, a Polish biochemist, who worked in London in 1912 and, upon realising their importance, he christened them *vitamines,* meaning 'essential to life'. By 1920, however, the 'e' was dropped and the word vitamin was born.

Generally vitamins are placed into one of two groups: fat soluble and water soluble.

Water soluble vitamins include the B complex group and vitamin C, both of which only remain in the body for a relatively short period of time as they are quickly absorbed through the intestine into the blood stream and any excess is passed out by the urine. Because of this they do therefore need to be replaced on a daily basis.

The fat soluble vitamins include A, D, E and K. Very little vitamin K can be stored in body, although vitamins A, D and E are absorbed with dietary fats and stored in the liver and fatty tissue where they can remain for up to a year or more.

Table 1.8, over on the next page, sets out each vitamin, its function and food sources, although it is beyond the remit of this book to provide recommended daily allowances.

Vitamin	Function	Food Source
A (Retinol – animal derived) (Betacarotene – vegetable derived)	Vital to good vision, immunity and healthy skin	Liver, Cod, Halibut, Eggs, Dairy, Green and Orange Fruit and Vegetables
B1 (Thiamine)	Assists in the function of the brain, nerve cells, digestion and the heart. Helps the body make use of protein.	Wheat Germ, Pork, Milk, Eggs, Yeast, Dried Beans, Watercress, sprouts, lamb Courgette, Asparagus, Mushrooms, Peas, Lettuce, Cauliflower, Cabbage, Tomatoes
B2 (Riboflavin)	Releases energy from food. Repairs and maintains healthy skin and nails. Regulates body acidity	Milk, Eggs, Meat, Leafy vegetables, Nuts, Liver, Mushrooms, Watercress, Bean Sprouts, Mackerel, Wheat Germ.
B3 (Niacin)	Maintains healthy skin, nerves and digestive system. Essential in energy production and brain function. Balances blood sugars and lowers cholesterol.	Peanuts, Poultry, Meats, Squash, Milk, Eggs, Whole Grains, Liver, Mushrooms, Asparagus, Cabbage, tomatoes, Cauliflower
B5 (Pantothenic Acid)	Involved in energy production, controls fat metabolism. Essential for brain and nerves. Helps make steroids (anti stress hormones). Maintains healthy skin and hair	Eggs, Dairy, Fish, cereals, Pulses, Yeast, Mushrooms, celery watercress broccoli, Cabbage, Tomatoes, Squash, Cauliflower, Alfalfa, Peas, Strawberries, Avocados
B6 (Pyridoxine)	Helps with chemical reactions between proteins and amino acids. Balances sex hormones, recommended during PMS or menopause. Natural anti-depressant	Bananas, Whole Grain Bread, Meat, Eggs, Dried Beans, Nuts, Seeds, Chicken, Fish, Liver, Peppers, Sprouts, Cabbage, Squash, Cauliflower, Water cress, Onions.

	and diuretic. Controls allergic reactions.	
B12 (cyanocobalamin)	Helps develop red blood cells and oxidise blood. Essential for nervous system and metabolising protein. Deals with toxins	Eggs, Shellfish, Fish, Meat, Milk, Poultry
Folic Acid	Critical during pregnancy for brain and nerve development Needed for utilising protein and red blood cell formation	Wheat Germ, Spinach, Nuts, Sprouts, asparagus, seeds, Broccoli, Cauliflower
Biotin	Helps body use essential fats, promotes healthy skin, hair and nerves.	Cauliflower, Lettuce, Peas, Tomatoes, Oysters, Grapefruit, Watermelon, Sweet corn, cabbage, Almonds, Cherries, eggs Herrings, Milk
C (Ascorbic Acid)	Promotes healthy gums, teeth, bones and connective tissue. Heals wounds, fights free radicals and strengthens immune system. Helps make anti-stress hormones	Citrus Fruits, Strawberries, Blackcurrants, Tomatoes, melons, Peppers, Potatoes, Broccoli, Peas, Peppers, Cauliflower
D (Ergocaliferol Cholecalciferol)	Promotes strong bones and teeth by retaining calcium	Cod Liver Oil, Oily Fish, Egg Yolk, Fortified Milk, Margarines
E (d-alpha tocopherol)	Protects tissue against oxidation. Prevents blood clots, improves wound healing and fertility. Recommended for skin.	Vegetable Oils, Sunflower Seeds, Nuts, Wheat Germ, Leafy Green Vegetables, Sea Food, Beans, Peas, Sweet Potatoes
K (Phylloquinone)	Necessary for normal blood clotting	Leafy Green Vegetables, Soya Beans, cereals Water Cress, Potatoes, Corn Oil, Tomatoes, Milk

Table 1.8

Minerals

Minerals and trace elements form the key components of our bodies and are present in tiny amounts in the soil, where they are absorbed by plant matter.

When we eat cereals, vegetables and fruit these essential elements make their way into our bodies where each one has its own particular function. The functions are too numerous to mention in this book, although in general terms minerals assist with:

- The formation of and continuing strength of bones and teeth.
- Production of blood cells and soft tissue
- Enzyme activity.
- Composition of bodily fluids.

It is important to realise that, unlike some vitamins, minerals and trace elements cannot be manufactured by the body or by the plants themselves and can only come from plants through absorption from the soil. Therefore, if the minerals are not present in the soil, they will be absent from the plant and hence from our diet.

Today's commercial farming methods mean that very few fields are left fallow to regenerate, which naturally depletes the soil. Farmers are only paid to replace three minerals, which include nitrogen, phosphorus and potassium, leaving a huge mineral void in our soil and this is the reason why many people make the decision to take supplements.

Fluid Intake

Fluid intake is vital to life and should therefore be given as much consideration as our food choices. Many people are under the impression that if they drink copious amounts of tea, coffee or carbonated drinks, their bodies will be well hydrated. Unfortunately drinks such as these can contain high amounts of caffeine, which act as a diuretic and actually dehydrate the body rather than hydrating it.

It is of the utmost importance that in addition to any of these drinks, we should ensure that we drink up to six glasses of water per day.

(Those with bladder or kidney disorders should seek the advice of their GP or a health professional).

The majority of us are chronically dehydrated most of the time, a fact which can be responsible for many symptoms of ill health, including general aches, pains and tiredness.

As human beings, our bodies comprise of approximately eighty percent water, and without sufficient daily intake we would quickly experience dehydration and die.

The following list details the benefits and importance of drinking water in order to maintain a healthy physiological and psychological function:

- It is the main constituent of the blood, lymph and bodily secretions.
- It transports nutrients, hormones, oxygen and antibodies through the circulatory and lymphatic systems and carries waste away.
- It aids digestion, absorption, circulation, respiration and excretion.
- It regulates body temperature.
- It maintains homeostasis.
- It maintains muscle tone.
- It helps with weight loss (the higher the water

intake the lower the amount of fat absorption).
- It helps maintain healthy skin.
- It helps to reduce pain, cholesterol and blood pressure.
- It helps to alleviate headaches, allergies, depression, chronic fatigue syndrome (ME), confusion, bloating, tiredness and colitis.
- It contains no fat, sugar or calories, therefore putting less strain on the body's digestive system.

Eating to Enhance Mood and Sexual Desire

Although natural foods are good for our overall health, some people choose specific foods or drinks in order to enhance their current mood and improve sexual performance, as is the case with alcohol and the consumption of foods classified as aphrodisiacs. An excess intake of either however can cause more problems than it alleviates.

Alcohol

In simple terms, alcohol is a drug without any nutritive qualities. The word 'alcohol' is a generic term for 'ethanol', which is produced by the fermentation of various foodstuffs such as barley, hops and grapes.

Ethanol produces intoxication because of its depressive effects on various areas of the brain, affecting physical performance, mood and behaviour, all of which become more noticeable with increased consumption. In the words of Shakespeare: 'It provoketh desire, but takes away the performance.'

Approximately twenty percent of ethanol is absorbed directly into the bloodstream from the stomach, whilst eighty percent is absorbed from the small intestine.

Therefore the longer ethanol remains in the stomach,

(i.e. when we eat food at the same time as drinking) the slower its absorption rate and the lower the peak in blood alcohol concentration.

Ethanol is highly soluble in water and absorbed much less in fat; therefore alcohol tends to distribute itself more successfully and evenly in water rich tissue.

A tall thin person weighing the same as a short fat person will feel fewer effects from the same alcohol consumption, due to the majority of their body tissue comprising of water.

Women have a naturally higher bodily fat content than men; therefore they will reach a higher blood alcohol concentration than men when consuming the same amount of alcohol.

Dependence on alcohol begins with the basic pleasure and reward circuits in the brain, which involve the chemical dopamine. These reward centres are designed to activate during pleasurable activities, however when they become activated more and more frequently there is a danger that addiction and dependence will result.

Aphrodisiacs

Mankind has been concerned with love and aphrodisiacs for as long as he has lived upon the earth and in all cultures, people have made love potions in order to bewitch the apple of their eye and to improve their own sexual performance.

In 400 BC the inhabitants of Greece practised love as a religion. As a result, two aspects of this religion were extremely important, viz: fertility and sexual performance, hence much time and effort was spent determining which foods would help to improve both.

Foods were chosen not only for the effect they had on the physical body, which modern nutritionists agree contain the necessary vitamins and minerals to help fertility or sexual virility, but in many cases were chosen simply for their suggestive shape, which would hopefully put those who consumed them in a sexually receptive state of mind.

In the sacred writings of the Hindus, Taoists and Zulus, the virtues of eating the correct foods in order to improve matters of love and sex are discussed in depth. The *Karma Sutra* states:

> *'Do not have a stomach full of food and drink, or you will have apoplexy and gout.... A man should eat strengthening foods, such as aromatic plants, meat, honey and eggs. A robust constitution is indispensable for copulation, but, above all, play with her lovingly, until she is excited and full of desire.'*

The word 'aphrodisiac' is named after the Greek goddess of love, beauty and sexuality. (The equivalent in Roman mythology is Venus). Aphrodite, it is said, rose from the foam of the sea on an oyster shell, thus giving rise to the first aphrodisiac food of oysters. Oysters are said to have a positive effect on the libido.

Some aphrodisiacs, such as rhinoceros horn, have, thankfully, long gone; however we do have a wide range of foods at our fingertips that are capable of enhancing our feelings when it comes to love.

Food	**Aphrodisiac Qualities**
Asparagus	Asparagus has been in cultivation since 200 BC and was highly regarded as an aphrodisiac by the Greeks, Romans and Russians. In the sixteenth century book, by Shaykh Umar Ibn Muhammed Al Nefzawi, *The Perfumed Garden,* we are told: '*With yolk of egg fried in fat, camel's milk and honey*

	(asparagus) causes the virile member to be on the alert, night and day.' In nineteenth century France, bridegrooms were served three courses of asparagus at their prenuptial dinner to ensure their virility.
Avocado	The Aztecs called the avocado *Ahuacuatl*, or 'testicle tree'. They thought the fruit hanging in pairs on the tree resembled the male's testicles. The Catholic priests in Spain found this fruit so obscenely sexual that they forbade it.
Banana	The word 'banana' is of African origin and in central parts of the country they are believed to be capable of fertilizing a woman of their own accord. If a woman can prove that a banana flower has fallen on her back, she is honourably acquitted of infidelity, as her actions can be attributed to the banana.
Chocolate	Originally made by the Peruvian Indians from the cacao bean, chocolate became the standard currency in Peru. In India, Montezuma, who had a harem of 600 odalisques, was said to have drunk fifty cups of chocolate a day from a gold goblet in order to maintain his virility. The Royal physician Henry Stubbs declared in the seventeenth century: 'Chocolate is provocative to lust.' Today research chemists agree that chocolate is a mild aphrodisiac as it excites the nervous system due to the fact that it contains *phenylethylamine*, the 'love chemical' which releases dopamine in the pleasure centers of the brain and peaks during orgasm.
Figs	Figs are considered to be an arousing stimulant and an open fig is said to emulate the female sex organs. Figs are one of the oldest recorded fruits. Adam and Eve covered their sexual organs with fig leaves and the ancient Greeks held them as sacred, associating them with love and fertility.
Honey	Sweet sticky honey is a great source of boron, a trace mineral that helps the body use and metabolise oestrogen, the female sex hormone. Studies have shown that this mineral may enhance testosterone levels in the blood, which is responsible for promoting sex drive and orgasm in both men and women. In the sixteenth century book by Nefzawi, *The Perfumed Garden,* we are told: 'Anoint the member with the blood of a he-goat mixed with honey, for a night of real splendour.'
Mussels	This was once the peasant's aphrodisiac and stems from

	the word 'mossel' which in medieval times also meant 'vulva'.
Oysters	Oysters have always been associated with enhanced sexual performance probably due to their high zinc content and its association with male fertility.
Root vegetables	Carrots and parsnips were valued as aphrodisiacs by not only the ancients but also by the Elizabethans who considered them to be: *'A great furtherer of Venus, her pleasure, and love's delight.'*
Spices	Many spices are thought to possess aphrodisiac qualities as we are told in a quote from *The Perfumed Garden* by Shaykh Umar Ibn Muhammed Al Nefzawi: 'Men who suddenly do not feel strong enough to enjoy women, should eat ginger, honey, byrether, hellebore, garlic, cinnamon, cloves, nutmeg, cardamoms, sparrow's tongues and long pepper immediately.'

Table 1.9

Eating for Religious Reasons and the Effects on Health

Food and drink laws have formed part and parcel of many religions throughout history, but to have an understanding of why these traditions came to be in place, we have to look at both their geographical location and the general food preservation techniques that were available at the time.

Many of the religious paths we accept as being orthodox today were born in the Middle and Far East, where the climate was not conducive to preserving certain fresh products. The leaders of the day, therefore, developed rules about the consumption of some food and drink products which gradually came to form part and parcel of religious customs.

Overeating was seen by many religious orders as gluttonous behaviour, whilst the consumption of alcoholic drinks or other oral stimulants were often regarded as being self-indulgent, all of which were frowned upon by the religious lawmakers. To try and steer people away from gluttonous practices, the ritual of fasting or restriction of certain foods and drink became prevalent within many of the world religions and is something that still holds sway today.

The laws regarding fasting or, at the very least, restriction of certain food types has been described as a 'call to holiness' by many religions and is often seen as a way of improving one's body in order to earn the approval of what certain religions call 'God' or 'Allah'. Fasting has also been used as a reminder of the poor and starving people of the world, a discipline designed to encourage people to resist temptation, an act of repentance for wrongdoings and as a cleansing procedure to drive evil from the body.

In more modern times most religions have come to accept that fasting can cause health problems and, as such, have relaxed the fasting rules for certain groups of people, such as pregnant and nursing mothers, young children, the elderly, those undertaking strenuous work and those suffering from certain illnesses, such as diabetes. For those who do fast, the intake of water is usually permitted, however during prolonged periods of fasting such as during Ramadan in the Islamic faith, excess acids can build up in the digestive system, which can result in a sour taste in the mouth, burning in the stomach and other symptoms of ill health.

With regards to the consumption of stimulants, opinion varies according to religion. A stimulant is categorised as anything that excites the nervous system and changes the physiology of the body, such as alcohol, drugs and caffeine. As such, these substances are prohibited by many religions because they are considered to be both addictive and harmful. Many religions also restrict the use of spices, pickles and food with added preservatives as they too are considered to be harmful and affect the natural flavour of the food.

Tobacco is also seen as a stimulant and as such is frowned upon, although the use of marijuana is an accepted part of Rastafarianism as they consider it to be 'the weed of wisdom', which also has healing properties.

In addition to the rules followed by traditional religions, there have been extreme practices carried out over the centuries by those who claim that they do not require food in order to survive and that to live by the grace of their Christian God alone is sufficient.

One such person was Therese Neumann, a German nun, born on 9 April, 1898, in the village of Konnersreuth in Bavaria Germany. After a series of traumatic falls as a child, Therese became blinded and bedridden, but still pursued her childhood dream of entering the Catholic Third Order of St Francis as soon as she was old enough.

On the 29 April, 1923, whilst in her mid-twenties, Therese regained her sight, a fact she put down to, Therese of Lisieux, whom she admired, becoming beatified in Rome. When Therese of Lisieux was fully canonised on May 17, 1925, Therese Neumann claimed that the saint had called to her, resulting in the disappearance of all her remaining ailments.

During the Lenten period of 1926, almost a year after her miraculous healing, Therese noticed a wound appear above her heart and claimed to have experienced a vision of Christ with three disciples. A few weeks later she again had a vision of Christ bearing the cross and, in addition to the wound above her heart, also noticed a wound on her left hand. Blood began to stain her clothing and she was no longer able to keep the information to herself.

On the Christian day of Good Friday, she witnessed

the crucifixion and displayed further wounds on her hands and feet, accompanied by blood flowing from her eyes. These wounds, or stigmata, did not appear to detrimentally affect her health and over subsequent years she continued to suffer the agonies of the crucifixion during the Lenten and Easter period of the Christian calendar. At the time of her death in 1962, the stigmata were still present, a fact which led her to become officially recognised as a Catholic mystic and stigmatic.

For a period of forty years between her first healing in 1922 and her death in 1962, Therese apparently consumed no food other than the Holy Eucharist and also claimed not to have drunk any water from 1926. In July 1927, a medical doctor and four Franciscan nurses kept a watch on her twenty four hours a day, for two weeks and confirmed that she had received neither food nor water except for one consecrated sacred host per day. She apparently had suffered no side effects, such as loss of weight or dehydration, and during the Second World War she refused to accept German ration cards saying she had no need of physical nourishment. According to a visit paid to Therese by the Yogi author Paramahansa Yogananda, she is said to have stated:

'*One of the reasons I am on earth today is to prove that man can live by God's invisible light and not by food only.*'

The Roman Catholic Church has neither confirmed nor denied the physical ailments from which she suffered or her stigmata, however her popularity has resulted in a request for her beatification and in 2005 formal proceedings were begun with the Vatican by the Bishop of Regensburg.

Dedication
For me, the sense of taste is symbolic of the element of fire, for it puts fire in my belly and fuels my energy reserves. It is the sense through which I can enjoy all the gifts of Mother Nature's bounty.

Taste reminds me of the changing seasons, for it allows me to experience the delights of summer through soft fruits, sweet seafood, lavender shortbread, herbal teas, sun blushed tomatoes, juicy olives and crisp salads.

When winter beckons, my food choices change to roasted vegetables, herb breads, nourishing soups and the luxury of a hot Irish whisky. Through the action of eating and drinking, I am able to nourish my physical body, the vehicle of my soul.

Dedication to the Goddess
The following is an example of how we can express our appreciation for our sense of taste. Light a red candle, symbolic of the base chakra, fire, and determination, placing beside it some form of food (homemade if possible), accompanied either by wine or grape juice and chant the following dedication:

Lady Goddess, gift bearer of the senses,
I appreciate and honour my sense of taste.
I give thanks to all the animals and plants that allow me to have nourishing food on my table.
I give thanks that through taste I am able to enjoy nature's bounty.
I give thanks that through taste my loved ones and I are nourished and healed.
Please accept this food as token of my gratitude.

Let the candle burn right down if possible. It may be a

generous gesture to give some form of food such as homemade cake or bread to a neighbour, friend or loved one or to make a donation to a local homeless centre to help out with their food bill.

Conclusion

Our food and drink choices are made for a myriad of different reasons, the majority of which are dependant upon our budget, emotional and psychological well-being, culture, religion, health concerns, ethical reasons, image and overall taste.

Whatever our food preferences, it is worth remembering that a well balanced diet with plenty of water will help to maintain not only a healthy body, but also impact dramatically on our emotional, psychological and spiritual well-being.

Mrs Darley Tale: The Cheese Farm

Even at seven thirty in the morning, the air smelled warm and, with the sun well risen, I wandered into the garden with a cup of tea in order to contemplate what I had to do for my dinner party later that evening.

'Good morning, dear,' called Mrs Darley appearing from behind the old pig sty wall with a huge bunch of nettles in a wicker basket.

'Oh, hello,' I replied, 'are you doing a bit of weeding?'

'Not exactly,' she said, 'I'm collecting these for the cheese farm.'

I looked at her with what must have been a blank expression.

'For the Yarg,' she said, obviously hoping that would clarify matters.

'Yarg', I repeated as a foreigner would a new word.

'Yes, dear. Yarg cheese, they make it at the farm down in Rilla Mill.'

'But why do they need nettles to make cheese?' I asked.

'Because that's what they finish the outside of the cheese with,' Mrs Darley explained. 'You've obviously never tried Yarg cheese then?'

I shook my head. 'No, and I'm not particularly sure that I really want to. Nettles aren't particularly high on my list of culinary "must tries".'

'Then you underestimate them, my dear,' said Mrs Darley. 'Nettles have been used for thousands of years for their medicinal properties.'

'Mmmm,' I murmured with a hint of scepticism, 'you'll forgive me if I'm not overly enamoured.'

'Don't knock it 'til you've tried it. Look, Phyllis and I are going down to the cheese farm this afternoon to take our nettles, why don't you come with us and take a look around; they do guided tours.'

I shook my head. 'Maybe another time,' I said, 'I've got guests for dinner tonight and I haven't even started to prepare anything yet.'

'Well, why don't you start now while it's still early and then join Phyllis and me this afternoon. We're not going out until two and,' she added, 'a nice piece of Yarg cheese after the meal will go down a treat with your guests.'

The idea of something different on the cheese board suddenly appealed to me and I heard myself agreeing to accompany Mrs Darley later in the day.

The farm was set in the pretty wooded valley of Rilla Mill and by mid-afternoon, Phyllis, Mrs Darley and I were pulling into the farmyard. After paying for our tickets, we were directed towards an old whitewashed barn, where we joined around half a dozen other people for a short introductory film. Following this we were taken on a fascinating tour of the cheese making process, which culminated in the decorating of the truckles of cheese with nettle leaves.

'All the nettles and wild garlic leaves we use for our cheeses are picked by hand in the rural areas, well away from any pollution,' our large and amenable host informed us. 'In fact, we always advertise in the local paper for nettle pickers at this time of year and these ladies here are two of our regular contributors,' he said gesturing towards Phyllis and Mrs Darley.

'Well we've not let you down today, Tony,' laughed Phyllis.

'Glad to hear it,' he smiled.

'So, why do we use nettles and stinging ones at that?' Tony rhetorically asked his audience. 'Well, firstly, and probably most importantly from our point of view, the nettles impart a unique flavour to the cheese, a sort of mushroomy taste. Secondly, they make a pretty form of decoration, mind you, we rinse and steam them before use, not just to cleanse them of insects and such like, but to make sure that they lose their sting, just in case any of you were worried that eating our cheese might be a painful experience! And thirdly, apart from their flavour, nettles also have health benefits as for hundreds of years they've been used to treat a whole range of ailments, from blood disorders to skin complaints and from sciatica to arthritis, which is probably why the Romans used to indulge in a little self-flagellation in the belief that it would ease their rheumatism.'

This was the point at which we all laughed, but winced simultaneously. At the end of the tour we were led into the shop where we were able to taste different varieties of cheese and I immediately purchased a large slice of traditional Yarg for the forthcoming dinner party.

Arriving back home, I declined Mrs Darley's offer of a drink as I still had pudding to prepare before my guests arrived, but as I was standing whisking a bowl of cream in the kitchen the familiar words, 'Hello, dear,' drifted through from the porch.

'Sorry to bother you,' Mrs Darley began as I walked towards the door, 'I know you're busy, but I just thought you might like to try this with a piece of saffron cake as it's still a few hours before you'll be eating.

'It's nettle tea and what Tony failed to tell you is, that nettle is a magickal plant, often used in spell craft for healing purposes, information that is better saved for when you have more time, but what I will just tell you is that they are full of vitamins A and C, so for someone who is always prone to colds,' she said pointedly, 'this has to be the brew for you.'

'Thank you,' I said peering into the mug and taking a drink of the liquid, which I expected to have an earthy mushroom taste. 'Oh,' I said in surprise as the unmistakable taste of Irish whisky filled my taste buds.

Mrs Darley smiled. 'I know nettles are good for you dear, but no one said they couldn't benefit from a helping hand when it comes to taste.'

Pleasures of the Flesh

For some, Sunday's are days of peace and quietude,
Of rest and deliberation.
For me, Sundays are days of passion,
Of hunger, of seduction.

The week is akin to a slow agonising death.
My life blood ebbs slowly away.

I grow weak with yearning,
Sick with love.

I will the hours to have Mercurial speed,
Until Sunday,
When I call for the clock to be still,
And my senses to awake.

I bring gifts; Rich dark wine
From the table of the Gods,
Sweet delights to consummate our union.
My excitement builds.

My eyes run greedily across your dusky form,
Senses heavy with anticipation.
I resist no longer.
My mouth tastes unadorned flesh.

I am besotted.
I am enchanted.
I am lost.

I have a wife.
A woman of great wit,
Of great virtue,
Of great beauty.

Of vegetarian persuasion.

Chapter 7

The Sense of Hearing

The Troubadour

Every night I come, to hear painted words
Fall from your lips upon the canvas of
My imagination, bleeding colours
Through my monochrome world as tales unfurl.

I fashion a crown of laurelled splendour
With which to honour the beauty of your
Infinite mind and, upon your lips, I
Bestow a kiss of honeyed eloquence.

Mrs Darley Tale: The Dream Maker

It was mid-September and the heat of the summer was beginning to give way to the more mellow days of autumn. I was sitting enjoying a glass of parsnip wine with Mrs Darley late one Saturday afternoon when the half stable door burst open and Lucy came tumbling breathlessly into the lounge.

'Oh hello, dear,' said Mrs Darley, 'is everything alright?'

'They're here!'

'Who are, dear?' Mrs Darley asked.

'The troubadours. I saw them this afternoon. The caravans are opposite *Long Tom*.'

I smiled, somewhat bemused at Lucy's obvious excitement. 'And who are the troubadours?' I asked.

'The most wonderful storytellers ever!' she said, her eyes bright with excitement. She turned to Mrs Darley, 'Mum's sent me round to ask when you'd like to go,'

'I don't mind, dear,' said Mrs Darley, 'but I expect you will want to go as soon as possible?'

'Tonight?' She suggested hopefully.

'Why not?' Mrs Darley laughed.

'Will you come?' Lucy turned to me.

'Of course she will,' Mrs Darley said.

'Well it sounds good to me,' I smiled immediately feeling myself caught up in Lucy's enthusiasm, 'and what's more, I'll even drive us up the lane.'

Lucy whooped with delight as she disappeared from view and I too took my leave with a promise to call round just before seven.

As dusk gathered, Lucy, Rose, Mrs Darley and I began to make our way across the uneven ground of Caradon Moor. Our destination was the fire that blazed in the near distance, silhouetting the curved rooves of the caravans against the reddening sky of the west.

'This looks like a good spot,' said Rose as we joined the growing crowd of people around one side of the fire. She threw the waterproof sheet onto the ground and within a few minutes we were all settled and clutching a small tot of whisky, courtesy of Mrs Darley, to keep out the cold.

The show began with the slow beating of a drum, which somehow always had the ability to awaken something primal in me and I felt a sense of deja vu as two hooded figures appeared from the darkness and became visible in the light of the fire. The drum beat quickened as they began to spin their way around the fire's perimeter, only falling silent when, having danced full circle, they finally came together in a puff of smoke from which a cloaked storyteller appeared.

'So,' he said in a voice that was almost a whisper, 'you came.'

There was something in the way he said the words and pointed his black gloved finger at what seemed like each and every one of us that made me shiver as I looked into his partially masked face.

'I knew you would,' he said, 'for although you may not know it, I called to each and every one of you in your dreams.'

I immediately took a sip of whisky for comfort and looked round at Lucy to see what effect the troubadour was having on her, but to my surprise she was smiling and her eyes shone with anticipation in the firelight.

'Tonight,' he continued, 'I will tell you the tale of Cob, guardian of the eastern well; The Dream Maker. Take heed, my friends, take heed and remember that what ever you put out to the world will come back, albeit often in strange ways.'

With these words of warning ringing in my ears the troubadour took his seat on an old log and drew his cloak tightly around him as he began his tale.

'Cob sat on the lowest ledge of the eastern well just above the waterline, his sharp pointed face cupped miserably in his hands. He looked down at the ring of black water and, just for once, wished he could drown, but naiads don't drown and, unless they take a drink from a human, naiads don't even die, they are water spirits and so, Cob continued to sit.

'Suddenly the sound of childlike voices from above disturbed his melancholy as a shower of silver coins ricocheted off his hat before plunging into their watery grave. Cob rubbed his head, "Damn those humans," he said, "with their constant wearying demands. Give me this; give me that, without so much as a thought for the poor naiad, duty bound in return for a silver coin, to help bring about their dearest wish."

'He stared into the black abyss and allowed himself to wallow in self-pity at the recent string of events, which led him to be sitting in the darkest, dankest part of the well, contemplating his fate.

'One day in early spring, when the sun was busy making rainbows dance across the waterfall, the summons came and Cob found himself standing before the council elect.

'A naiad with a considerably large head leaned forward and used the word "promotion" as though it was a good thing and Cob felt the death knell of freedom ring in his ears.

'His promotion was to that of "dream maker to the humankind" and he was to take up his new position at the eastern well under the initial guidance of Canderwall, an aged naiad whose beard was as long as time.

'"A dream maker," Canderwall explained, "is one who takes care of human wishes in exchange for a silver coin but …," he paused for dramatic impact, "the wish business isn't quite as straight forward as you might think. There are three important rules that must be adhered to at all times and to break them all is to face the ultimate punishment."

'Cob didn't like rules and raised an anxious eyebrow, "... and the rules are?"

'"The rules are, number one, you must never reveal yourself to the humankind and must stay hidden within the confines of the well."

'Cob thought that sounded fairly easy and nodded.

'"Number two, you must never give the humankind what they ask for directly, you may only guide them to find the way for themselves."

'"What do you mean?" asked Cob.

'"Well, we are never allowed to interfere in the karma of the humankind, but we can help them to find what they are looking for through their own life experience. For example, if someone wishes to pass their exams, it is quite unacceptable for you to provide the answers, although of course we could lead them to discovering natural ways of improving their memory and retaining information."

'"How?" Cob asked.

'"Like this," Canderwall bent down and plucked a sprig from a bank of herbs. "Smell," he offered it to Cob.

'"What is it?" Cob asked as he buried his nose into the greenery.

'"Rosemary," Canderwall quickly answered, "for remembrance, or you could try this."

'He offered Cob a second bunch of herbs.

'"Peppermint?" Cob asked.

'Canderwall smiled. "Yes, to sharpen the mind and make it more receptive to learning."

'Cob nodded, "I'm beginning to understand."

'"Good," Canderwall smiled, "and rule number three states that you must never, but never, look into the human soul."

'"I wouldn't know how," Cob said.

'"Ah," said Canderwall, sitting down alongside the stream, "it is said that the eyes of the human kind reflect the gateway to their soul and when elementals such as us see human eyes reflected in a body of water, we are able to access their deepest desires, their soul's destiny."

'"And why is that so bad?" asked Cob.

'"Because no one has the right to access the soul of another, not even fairy folk and the punishment for all these misdemeanours is severe."

'"How severe?" asked Cob, feeling increasingly unsure of his new position as dream maker of the eastern well.

'"Well, the council have decreed that anyone breaking these rules will be destined to spend their life tantalisingly close to water, yet will never again be allowed to enter."

'A cold hand momentarily touched Cob's heart, for a naiad to spend his life without feeling water on his body was not even worth contemplating and he immediately vowed that these were three rules he would never break.

'But Cob should have realised, he should never say never.

'With his training underway, Cob had taken up position on a beautiful fern, seven bricks down from the top of the well, where he was both able to hear the human wish and see the colour of their money. As a result he had steered people towards healing waters and herbs, made a quiet place by the deep pool in which they could contemplate and helped them find inspiration within the beauty and stillness of the woods.

'On his seventh afternoon as trainee dream maker, he looked up at the lengthening shadows and knew that his working day was almost over, but just as he was about to leave, he happened to look up into the face of a teenage girl peering down into the well and quickly took refuge under a convenient fern. He saw the shadow of her hand hover momentarily above the abyss, but just as she was about to cast her coin and utter her deepest wish, she abruptly disappeared, an occurrence which coincided with the raised voice of a man, who was making it clear in no uncertain terms that wishing wells were not where she was meant to be spending her time.

'Cob sighed and, feeling concerned for the girl, yet knowing it was not his place to interfere, he waited until silence reigned and finally left the well in order to refresh his tired body in the stream.

'The following day at dawn, Cob once again assumed his position seven bricks down from the top of the well and waited. This was the human equivalent of rush hour, for breakfast time was very popular for wish making and this morning was no exception. Whispers of business deals, colleague relationships, and successful interviews all found themselves spiralling down into the well accompanied by the obligatory silver coin.

'Just as Cob thought the immediate rush was over, a silver coin whistled past his ear and a familiar voice began to utter the words, "I need to escape, I have to get…"

'Forgetting himself for a moment, he peered out from beneath the cover of his fern and once again caught a glimpse of the girl he had seen the previous afternoon. Within an instant the same familiar raised male voice told her in no uncertain terms that what she was doing was ludicrous and Cob watched as she was violently pulled away from the edge of the well.

'Cob could feel a cold fingered anger building in his stomach and, momentarily forgetting himself, he left the confines of the well and flew up to the surface where he saw the girl being unceremoniously dragged towards the dark pool by a blond haired man in a business suit.

'"You like looking into water, Miranda?" he whispered menacingly into her ear. "Then look into this."

'He plunged her head into the dark pool and within an instant, Cob managed to break all three rules of the council elect.

'He immediately ran forward, forgetting that he

should never reveal himself to humankind and, without a second thought, he directly used his magickal powers to free Miranda from the man's vicelike grip. Feeling so incensed by what he had seen and being horrified by the tangible anger that oozed from Miranda's assailant, Cob glanced down into the dark pool and saw the man's eyes reflected in the water, revealing the dark secrets hidden within his soul.

'Retribution by the council elect was both swift and severe and within a few hours, Cob found himself, wings clipped, sitting on the lowest ledge of the eastern well, just above the waterline. Here he was destined to spend his days, tantalisingly close to the water, but never again to feel its coolness on his body. He pulled his hat down over his face and, for a moment, fervently wished that someone would grant him a wish, but knew in his heart that that would never happen.

'But you know what they say', the troubadour swiftly rose to his feet and walked around the circle pointing his black gloved hand once more at the audience who murmured almost trancelike, "Never say never".

'As Cob continued to sit just above the waterline, he became aware of a soft voice echoing around the well.

'"Thank you. I don't know who you are, or what you are, but thank you for saving my life. I just wish I could repay you in some way...."

'The voice broke and Cob's heart wept, for he knew that this was Miranda and that he was unable to make himself known to her for he could no longer fly. He looked down into the well and wished with all his heart that he could die.

'As he continued to stare into the blackness he became aware that the usually still circle of water was rippling and thought for a moment that that it was raining, but he could see that the sun was still out from the way the shadows danced on the wall of the well. Suddenly, however, he became aware from the distant muffled sobs that Miranda was crying.

'Within a moment, the realisation of what this meant dawned on him, for through her tears he could accept a drink from a human, an act which would finally end his miserable fate and so, leaning out as far as he could from his dank ledge, he shouted his thanks to Miranda, lifted his face and drank of her falling tears.'

'No!' Lucy's cry of despair caught us all by surprise.

'Ah,' the troubadour spun round and pointed his black finger at her, 'you wanted Cob to be a hero? To be saved?'

Lucy nodded.

'But Cob was a hero, my child, and he *was* saved, from a fate which, to him, was worse than death itself.'

An uncanny hush descended over the assembled crowd as the troubadour allowed his words to settle on the still night air before continuing.

'And so, my good people of Bodmin Moor, it is time to draw the veil of time across this poignant tale. But, let me leave you with this parting thought. Wishes, if they are heartfelt enough, really can come true, especially if you remember …' He spun round and once again pointed his black gloved hand at each and every one of us as we all murmured, '... never say never.'

'And what did you think of the troubadour?' Mrs Darley asked as we walking through the five barred gate on our way back to the cottages.

'I thought he was wonderful,' I said. 'He certainly gave me something to think about, to say it was just a fairy story.'

'Ah, but fairy stories have the ability to speak directly

to the subconscious mind, my dear, and, in so doing, have the power to touch our soul.'

'And once again, death comes as the healer,' I mused, remembering our conversation of several weeks ago.

Mrs Darley smiled. 'Indeed, my dear,' she said. 'Goodnight.'

Introducing the Sense of Hearing

Although there are many places on earth which we may describe as silent, it is, in fact, virtually impossible to find anywhere on this planet where silence can be 'heard'. Indeed if the scientists are to be believed, there are very few places in the universe where silence is a possibility, for the universe itself, a vibrating entity, creates sound.

As we lie suspended in the warm amniotic fluid of our mother's womb, our experience is one of both sound and vibration and, because sound travels approximately five times faster through water than air (1,500 meters per second as opposed to 340 meters per second), the sounds that we actually hear at this stage of our lives become deeply embedded in the subconscious mind. Therefore the sound of water, a heartbeat and the human voice become our first experience of what we term to be 'primordial sounds' and have the ability to awaken deep levels of recognition in the subconscious mind, regardless of race, sex or language.

Sound therapists have discovered that when these primordial sounds are either slowed down or speeded up, the conscious mind fails to recognise them. They are, however, still recognisable by the sub-conscious mind, which responds by showing a more relaxed brainwave pattern on an EEG.

When recordings of people speaking are doubled in speed and raised by three octaves, they sound like birds chirping and when they are raised by eight octaves the sound changes to that of crickets. Conversely when the human voice is slowed down twice from normal speed and reduced by three octaves, it resembles the sound of dolphins, whilst slowed by eight octaves it sound like the ebb and flow of the ocean. This offers an explanation as to why we are soothed by the sounds of nature.

The eminent psychiatrist Dr Carl Jung said that we all have the ability to tap into the 'collective unconscious', which he described as being a universal unconscious mind, greater and deeper than our own individual consciousness. Within this collective unconscious we are able to recognise primordial images such as symbols and sounds that are common to us all. In this way he saw the universe as one organic being, with all parts being designed from the same blueprint.

In 1989, Dr Jeffrey Thompson, a leading doctor in sound healing in the USA, came into contact with vibrational recordings taken from the Voyager spacecraft as it passed Jupiter, Saturn, Uranus and Neptune. When these vibrational recordings, which comprised of electromagnetic particles from the magnetic fields of the planets, were translated into sounds, many were found to resemble the ocean, dolphins, human voices, birds and crickets. Other sounds were also present, some of which, although strangely familiar, have yet to be identified. The rings of Uranus, meanwhile, produced a sound like Tibetan singing bowls.

The majority of us take everyday sounds for granted, but just how important is sound in our daily lives and can it have the ability to both harm and heal? The old adage 'sticks and stones may break my bones, but words will never hurt me' is, I feel, somewhat misguided.

We all accept that we can be injured by someone

initiating a physical attack; however the emotional and psychological hurt that can be caused through words can be far more long lasting, not to mention the damage caused to the subtle energy fields. A kind word is, therefore, invaluable and worth its weight in gold. If we could all find something positive to say to those we meet, the world would be both a happier and healthier place to live as our energy bodies would become stronger and more vibrant.

Understanding the Sense of Hearing

The sense of hearing is the fourth sense to develop at around sixteen weeks in the womb and is one of the most complicated.

In order to make a sound, an object has to vibrate. This vibration takes the form of rhythmic waves, which are measured in cycles per second (hertz). The range of normal human hearing begins at the lower limit of around sixteen hertz, whilst our top range varies at between 16,000 and 20,000 hertz.

Just because we are unable to perceive a sound from something, however, does not mean that it is not vibrating and creating a sound. Dolphins are able to perceive sounds which vibrate at 180,000 hertz, approximately ten times that which is audible by the human ear.

The ears form the entrance way to our auditory equipment and are the most incredible sensory organs, which perform three tasks in order for us to hear sound:

1. They direct sound waves into the correct part of the ear.
2. They sense fluctuations in air pressure.
3. They translate the fluctuations into an electrical

impulse, which the brain can understand.

The part of the ear specifically designed to catch and direct sound waves is known as the *pinna*, which is the curvaceous outer part of the ear. It is deliberately shaped to determine the direction of a specific sound. If a sound is coming from behind or above, it will bounce off the pinna in a different way to if it is coming from in front or below and will, therefore, alter the pattern of the sound wave.

Once the sound waves travel into the ear canal they come in contact with a thin, cone shaped piece of skin called the *tympanic membrane* or 'eardrum', beyond which lies the middle ear. The eardrum is exposed to air pressure not only from the outer ear and the atmosphere, but also from the middle ear, for air flows into the middle ear via the mouth and throat, thus keeping air pressure on both sides of the ear drum equal and allowing it to move freely back and forth. The ear drum is attached to the *tensor typani* muscle, which ensures that it remains taut.

The eardrum also protects the ear, for it masks loud, low-pitched background noise in order that we are able to concentrate on higher pitched sound, such as allowing us the ability to carry on a conversation whilst in noisy surroundings.

Before the sound passes to the inner ear, the *ossicles*, a group of tiny bones situated in the middle ear, have the job of amplifying the sound. When the eardrum vibrates, these little bones also begin to move, until the *cochlea fluid* is pulled towards the inner ear, thus creating waves which mirror the air pressure fluctuations of the sound wave.

Within the cochlea is the *basilar membrane,* compris-ing of between 20,000 and 30,000 reed-like fibres, which begin close to the middle ear as being short and stiff and respond to higher frequency waves. They gradually become longer and more flexible, which enables them to respond to lower frequency waves.

The cochlea is also lined with thousands of tiny hairs called the *organ of corti,* which react to frequency waves. When the hairs are moved, they send an electrical impulse through the cochlea nerve to the cerebral cortex, where the brain then interprets them, thus determining the loudness and the pitch of the sound based on the amount of hairs moved and their position.

Perhaps one of the most remarkable things about the whole process of auditory perception is that it is completely mechanical and relies totally upon physical movement, unlike the senses of taste, smell and vision which all involve chemical reactions.

The History of Sound in Healing and Creation Myths

The power of sound has been utilised by human beings in order to access deeper states of consciousness, expand awareness and heal the physical body for thousands of years and has been achieved in numerous ways from chanting and singing to drumming and the playing of musical instruments.

Sound works on the principal that everything in the universe is vibrating energy and it is a tool which can help to gradually move us through the lower energies of guilt, jealousy and fear in order to experience the higher vibrations of joy, peace and love.

Many of the creation myths from across the world use sound as the one vibration which brought life into being. The Christian Bible tells us in John 1:1: 'In the beginning was the word and the word was with God and the word was God.'

A similar quotation comes from the Vedic texts which tell us: 'In the beginning was Brahman with whom was the word.'

In America, the Zuni and Hopi Indians worshipped the goddess as a great spider. In their creation myth, the grandmother spider took some earth and mixed it with saliva. She then covered it with a magickal white cape, made from creative wisdom and sang over it her creation song. Two beings formed from this magickal act, the first solidified the earth, whilst the other, whom she named Echo, made the world resonate with the forces of sound and thus life came to the world.

In Tibetan and Hindu mythology it is the goddess of music, medicine, science and sound, Saraswati, the consort of Brahma, who sang the universe into being. In Egyptian myth, Thoth only had to speak the name of a being and it would manifest.

Many ancient cultures have used sound in both their ritualistic ceremonies and healing practices. The Australian Aborigines have used their unique instrument, the *yidaki,* or didgeridoo as it is now known, for over 40,000 years for a variety of purposes, but not least in attempting to heal illnesses of every kind. It has now been acknowledged that the sound vibrations made from the didgeridoo are in line with modern sound healing technology.

The Egyptian and Babylonian cultures used drums and rattles to bring about healing, a musical combination that is again appreciated in modern sound healing as the low frequency of the drums and the high vibration of the rattles form a 'harmonic', which is known to accelerate healing.

It is thought that in Atlantean times, sound was used for the purpose of healing and subsequent masters have since tapped into this ancient knowledge. The Greek philosopher and mathematician Pythagoras is often identified as being the first person to use sound as medicine. Pythagoras' preferred instruments were those of the flute and the lyre and he is credited with being the first person to understand the power of a musical interval (the pause between one note and another). A Greek writer of the time said:

'Pythagoras considered that music contributed greatly to health, if used in the right way. He called his method, 'musical medicine'. To the accompaniment of Pythagoras his followers would sing in unison certain chants. At other times his disciples employed music as medicine with certain melodies composed to cure the passions of the psyche...anger and aggression.'

As a mathematician with a strong interest in astronomy, Pythagoras appreciated that the movements of the planets through space created sounds and that this 'music of the spheres', with which he is famously associated, could be played on a single stringed instrument, which he himself invented, called the monochord. He is quoted as saying:
'There is geometry in the humming of the strings. There is music in the spacing of the spheres.'

Asclepiades, a Greek physician, added music to his aromatic massages as he thought it induced relaxation in the patient and helped to speed the healing process. Shamans, meanwhile, created a trance in which they travelled to the world of spirit through chanting or drumming.

In both Sufi and Vedic traditions, the inner nature of music is still practised in order to heal numerous health conditions and to reach sublime states of self realisation.

During the reign of Elizabeth I, Dr Thomas Campion practiced both lyrical and vocal compositions for the purpose of healing his patients, whilst the famous composer Handel was quoted as saying:

'I do not wish to amuse my audience; I wish to make them better.'

Taking matters one step further, the composer Alexander Skryabin composed a work especially designed to remove all past karma from those attending his performance.

Today sound healing is a scientifically recognised and respected healing modality, with research confirming facts that the ancients simply accepted.

Exploring Sound Healing

Cymatics is the word given to the study of sound vibration by Dr Hans Jenny, a Swiss medical doctor who, during the 1960s, spent much of his spare time observing the effects of sound upon matter. The word itself is Greek for 'waveform' and is descriptive of the way in which sound moves.

Cymatics is based upon the fundamental law of resonance, in that each organ of the body has a specific healthy 'sound' or vibrationary rate. When the body becomes diseased, this vibrationary rate changes, and becomes like an instrument that is out of tune. If, however, the correct vibration is applied to the body through the use of sound, then this will encourage the body to once again return to its healthy state.

The literary critic and cultural philosopher Rudolf Steiner (1861-1925), considered to be one of histories most original thinkers, said:

'There will come a time when a diseased condition will not be described as it is today by physicians and psychologists, but it will be spoken of in musical terms, as one would speak of a piano that was out of tune.'

Mr Masaru Emoto, the Japanese best selling author of *Messages from Water* demonstrated that just like human beings, water molecules are also affected by sound and intention. Emoto found that clean water molecules take the form of beautiful geometric crystal snowflakes, whilst polluted water takes the form of mud. He decided to see whether different sounds would alter the shape of the molecular structure.

He placed distilled water between two speakers for several hours, whilst playing different types of music and then photographed the crystals that formed after the water was frozen. He discovered that when *Air on a G string* was played, the resulting frozen molecule had formed into a beautiful geometric shape, very much like a clear crystal snowflake, whilst the molecule that had been exposed to heavy metal music formed a blurred confused image.

Mr Emoto also wanted to measure the effect of sacred words on a molecule of water and took water molecules from the polluted Fujiwara Dam in Japan, which initially looked like muddy blobs. He then asked Buddhist monks to chant a sacred prayer over the water and was delighted to see the molecular structure change back into a crystal clear geometric shape, concluding that through intent and healing words, polluted water could be restored to its natural geometric symmetry.

Since the body comprises of eighty percent water and

sound travels five times faster through water than air, it becomes easy to appreciate how sound is able to create beneficial change in the body.

Sound research carried out by Fabien Maman, a French acupuncturist and sound healer, documented in his book *The Role of Music in the 21st Century* that when all the notes of the ascending chromatic scale, i.e. C, C#, D, E, E flat, F, F#, G, A, B and B flat were played to 'normal cells' on a xylophone, each note affected the cells differently, creating a different shape and brightening their auric colour. In contrast, cancerous haemoglobin cells became unstable and began to disintegrate.

With the use of EEG tests, (measurement of changes in brainwave patterns), and blood chemistry screening tests, scientists are now able to see the effect that sound has on the mind and body in both different states of health and different states of consciousness. The results of many trials and studies have shown that by introducing specific sounds into daily meditation sessions of twenty minutes, blood pressure becomes regulated, immune responses increase and feelings of well-being are experienced.

In California, university lecturer and Nobel Prize winner Dr James Gimzewski uses an atomic microphone in order to listen to sound emitted by cells, a process he has called *sonocytology*. This new science maps the pulsations of a cell's outer membrane, therefore having the ability to identify the 'song of the cell'. Gimzewski has discovered that every cell in our body has a unique sonic signature and 'sings' to its neighbours.

Sonocytology is not only a powerful diagnostic tool for identifying diseased cells, but it also has the ability to play the destructive sound that the diseased cells make back to them greatly amplified, thereby causing them to implode and self destruct. The healthy cells surrounding the diseased ones are not affected, for they are vibrating at a completely different frequency. Dr Gimzewski considers audible sound therapy to potentially be the greatest natural modality in non-invasive healing.

The use of sound in orthodox medicine is becoming more widely accepted as both gallstones and kidney stones are broken up using a machine known as a lithotripter. This machine bombards the stones with a specific frequency for a period of between one to two hours until they are small enough to be passed out through the urine without the need for either anaesthetic or surgery.

The Benefits of Sound Healing

Everyone, regardless of age, can benefit from music therapy, despite whether they heal their symptoms completely or simply experience a few moments of relief. Music can be of comfort to those entering our world, to those leaving it and assists each one of us in coping with our daily lives at any stage in between.

Some hospitals and care homes now appreciate the healing power of therapeutic sound, regardless of whether it has been scientifically proved or accepted by orthodox practitioners. Hopefully this awareness will continue to grow and shine a light in a many a patient's otherwise dark world.

In one American hospital, the premature baby unit is experimenting with the effect that music has on what can often be an extremely stressful environment. Under normal circumstances the medical profession are scurrying about, parents are upset and anxious, medical equipment is bleeping, babies are crying and there is very little opportunity to rest for these babies who are fighting for the gift of life. Into this mayhem, however, they have introduced a harpist and have monitored the profound effect that just a few moments of gentle playing has had on the whole environment. Babies fall asleep, parents feel relief, the bleeping of monitors subsequently reduce and nurses feel less stressed.

Similarly in care homes, the lives of the inhabitants have very little to engage them, especially if they suffer from dementia or Alzheimer's disease and much of their time is spent either in torment, or staring into space.

The introduction of familiar music into such an environment is both soothing and stimulating and, even for the most severely affected patients, flickers of recognition often pass across their faces as they begin to sway in time to the music. The music helps them to connect to happier times, providing respite from the often frightening and unrecognisable world they find themselves in.

Within a general hospital environment, the use of music both before and after surgery has shown that patients require less anaesthetic, awake from anaesthesia more quickly, experience fewer side effects and heal more rapidly.

Patients recovering from heart attacks and strokes appear to respond more effectively to treatment when listening to music, whilst those suffering from chronic conditions such as back pain, fibromyalgia and chronic fatigue syndrome find more relief during physical therapy when this is accompanied by music.

Those experiencing emotional disorders such as depression, anxiety, grief, anger and loneliness need less medication and have more success during psychotherapy sessions when music is played during their treatments.

Likewise, children with learning disabilities show a marked improvement in maths, reading and reasoning skills when they are exposed to sound therapy. Interestingly, the results for improvement increase dramatically when the children are encouraged to make music themselves.

For those who are deaf, music can still play an important part of their lives. According to experiments carried out on both deaf and hearing people at the National Technical Institute for the Deaf in Rochester New York by Dr Dean Shibata, Professor of Radiology at the University of Washington, deaf people experience vibration in the area of the brain that is used for hearing in people who are not deaf, hence their ability to sense music. The same institute gives deaf audience members balloons to hold with their fingertips when they attend a concert, in order that they can feel the vibration of the music.

A multi-sensory sound lab has also been developed, which enables students to experience sound on several levels. The lab processes sound waves and sends them to loudspeakers, which are placed face down on a platform.

The people standing on that platform can then experience sound as vibrations, which are slow if the notes are low and which get increasingly faster as the notes get higher.

To accompany these vibrations, a spectrum analyser and oscilloscope depict the sound waves as colour and design, thus making it a multi-sensory experience. It is also being used to provide training in modern dance by enabling deaf students to feel the rhythm.

The most famous of all composers to experience deafness was Beethoven, who lost his hearing in middle age although this did not prevent him from continuing his career as a composer as he was able to 'hear' the sound of each note in his head.

Perhaps the most well known deaf musician today is Evelyn Glennie, the world renowned percussionist. Glennie describes herself as 'profoundly' deaf as opposed to 'totally' deaf and says that she is able to 'hear' with various parts of her body. She plays her instruments bare footed and is able to distinguish the pitch of a note from where she feels it in her body.

To enable us to truly benefit from sound healing, despite whether we have the sense of hearing or not, it is important that we actually listen to, or feel the sounds being produced.

In order to do this we have to switch off the vibrations of everyday life such as the washing machine, the kettle, the TV and the iPod, for only then are we able to 'listen' not only with our ears, but also with our heart and it is at this point that true healing begins to take place.

Music is one of the most powerful catalysts for healing because it has the ability to touch us on a soul level and subsequently radiate out through the subsequent layers of mind, emotions and body, thereby bringing healing to all levels of our being.

Just look at the way babies react to a gentle lullaby or the soft humming of a nursery rhyme.

The Chinese have an ancient saying: 'There will come a time when man will be known by his sound, not by his name.'

Types of Sound Healing

Sound healing involves the therapeutic application of sound frequencies, with the sole intention of restoring balance in the subtle energy fields and beneficially affecting us on a mind, body and spirit level. The chosen sound can be administered in a variety of ways, examples of which are listed below with the most popular explored in more detail:

- The human voice (singing or mantric chanting).
- Toning and overtoning (listening to the vocally created sounds of a practitioner).
- Music therapy (specific songs or pieces of music are selected to bring about changes in emotions or behaviour).
- Music in imagery (combining sound with visualization).
- Didgeridoo.
- Tibetan singing bowls or bells.
- Gongs.
- Tuning forks.
- Somatic instrument (direct application of sound on the body to initiate healing).
- Electronic ear (listening to specifically filtered music through headphones in order to stimulate the ear and neural pathways to open up the brain. Effective with learning disabilities, dyslexia and emotional issues).
- Sonic entrainment or Cymatic therapy (Vibrations of sound are applied to the body to stimulate a specific area).
- Harmonic resonance (application of synthesized sounds following muscle testing).
- Bio acoustics (missing frequencies' of client's voice are found and played back via synthesized sounds)
- Hemi-synch (client listens to synthesized sounds to balance the hemi-spheres of the brain)

- Vibro-acoustic beds or chairs (music is projected into the body via chair or bed).

Music Therapy

The music we choose to listen to often depends both upon our mood and what we wish to achieve from it. When we think of 'healing sounds', we automatically think of something soothing; however, if we want to be kept awake because we have a long drive home, then something stimulating might be more beneficial.

Generally there are certain pieces of music which are accepted as bringing about balance and healing, due to their specific frequencies. Many of these pieces tend to pulse at sixty hertz per minute, which induces the alpha state of relaxation and include Baroque music (adagio sections) and some new age compositions.

The director of Baltimore Hospital's coronary care unit states that half an hour of classical music is capable of producing the same effect as ten milligrams of Valium. The *Journal of the American Medical Association* reported that pregnant mothers who listened to classical music during childbirth did not require anaesthetic, as the music encouraged the release of endorphins in the brain, thus reducing pain and anxiety. In another study, the heart rate of babies in the womb was monitored whilst different types of music were played. It was shown that when rock music was played, the babies became agitated, whilst when Vivaldi or Mozart was played, they would return to a state of utmost calm.

Towards the end of the twentieth century, there was much talk about Mozart and the healing properties of his music due to the success of a book entitled *The Mozart Effect* by Don Campbell. In 1993, researchers at the University of California carried out experiments on this effect and found that college students who listened to ten minutes of Mozart's *Sonata for two pianos in D major K448* before taking an IQ test scored nine points higher than when they had previously listened to relaxation tapes or sat in silence.

Likewise, King George I, during the early eighteenth century, felt he would be able to make better decisions if only he could listen to the right kind of music and it was this that led Handel to compose his *Water Music Suites*, which the king played whilst cruising down the Thames on his royal barge.

According to Dr Alfred Tomatis, the French ear, nose and throat surgeon, Mozart's *Five Violin Concerti* are at the top of the list as far as bestowing healing properties upon the listener are concerned. These concerti were responsible for healing many opera singers who exhibited various physical symptoms which affected their vocal performance. This is thought to be due to the fact that Mozart's violin concertos contain the perfect range of pitches and tones to heal both the voice and the individual. They encourage both sides of the brain to work together, thus overcoming the left brain dominance of our Western society and also encourage the firing patterns of neurons in the cerebral cortex thereby improving concentration and increasing the ability to intuit.

Listening to music is only one way of receiving music therapy, playing an instrument is another. It is said that Albert Einstein was an average student until he began to play the violin. It appears that the playing of an instrument gave a freedom to his mind that enabled him to come up with some remarkable ideas.

In 1993, researchers at Irvine's Centre for Neurobiology of Learning and Memory found that children under five who had been having music lessons, scored eighty percent higher on object assembly tasks than those who had received no musical training.

Drumming

Drum therapy is an ancient healing modality that stretches back thousands of years and was recognised by many cultures, from the Shamans of Mongolia to the Minianka tribe of West Africa. Drumming utilised rhythm to promote both healing and self expression, a fact which is now recognised by today's sound therapists.

Drumming has been shown in numerous studies to assist in cases of stress, Alzheimer's disease, autism, addiction, fatigue, anxiety, asthma, chronic pain, arthritis, migraine, some cancers, MS, Parkinson's disease, stroke, paralysis and a host of other serious disorders. A leading cancer expert in the USA, Dr Barry Bittman, encourages his patients, upon diagnosis, to join a drumming group and was quoted as saying:

'Group drumming tunes our biology, orchestrates our immunity, and enables healing to begin.'

Group drumming also has the added benefit of helping us feel connected to others, which, at times of illness or stress, may sometimes be lacking, as patients can feel increasingly isolated from the world.

Research demonstrates that rhythmic energy to the brain synchronises the two cerebral hemispheres, allowing the suppressed subconscious to express itself through conscious awareness, therefore leading to a deeper understanding of the inner self. It also encourages the production of endorphins and endogenous opiates to bring about feelings of well-being.

Drumming is a rhythmic occupation, with the word 'rhythm' coming from the Greek word *rhuthmos,* meaning 'to flow'. Drumming, therefore, enables us to reconnect with the flow of life, energising our subtle energy field, bringing relief to the physical body and releasing both emotional trauma and negative thought patterns.

Tibetan Singing Bowls

Tibetan singing bowls create the most beautiful sounds, which seem to emanate from nowhere and yet appear to be everywhere.

Today there are many types of singing bowls available, from the ancient bowls of Tibet, Bhutan and Nepal to machine made ones and the more modern and expensive crystal singing bowls.

Some ancient singing bowls date back hundreds of years, although their exact ages are unknown. They were made from a seven metal alloy and had, during their creation, sacred prayers and mantras chanted over them for the specific purposes of healing and transforming consciousness, which became woven into the fabric of the bowl.

By contrast, the new metal and crystal bowls are machine made and are therefore devoid of being charged with sacred words. That does not, though, detract from the sound, as this can be quite beautiful and, coupled with the intent of the user, still make an excellent healing tool.

The application of sound through singing bowls can be made in several ways. Some practitioners supply a 'sound bath', where clients simply listen to the playing of the bowls whilst lying down and relaxing. Others move the bowls up and down the client's body to listen for a change in sound. These changes indicate an area of imbalance and the bowls are then played in that area until it becomes harmonious again. Some practitioners use one bowl, whilst others use various bowls often laid upon the head and body of the client.

The sound that emanates from a singing bowl is primarily 'OM', or also known as 'AUM', and it is generally considered that these vibrations have the ability to promote relaxation and realign the subtle energy bodies which, in turn, affects the health of the client on all levels.

Bells (called Ghanta in Sanskrit) too have been used in Buddhist meditation for centuries and comprise of two bells strung together. When rung, they sound slightly out of tune with each other, resulting in the creation of a sound that takes the brainwaves into a meditative state (practice of zazen).

The Human Voice and the importance of Chants, Mantras and Harmonics

The human voice is the ultimate healing instrument and, to a degree, we each have the ability to create pure tones and vocal harmonics. There is a Sufi saying: 'The voice is the only instrument made by God. All other instruments were made by man.'

Research in the USA has shown that when certain vocal tones sound under stress in our voice, these appear to correspond to imbalances in our physical body. By changing our voice tone, our brain wave frequencies also change which, in turn, begins to eliminate illness.

In her book *Toning the Creative Power of the Voice*, Laurel Elizabeth Keys explains that a weak voice signifies negativity, which attracts illnesses such as cancer, asthma, allergies, tumours and arthritis and that until a person reverses their tonal pattern then healing remains elusive.

Toning is defined as 'making a sound with an elongated vowel for an extended period'. It is an easily learned skill and, once mastered, oxygenates the body, deepens breathing, relaxes muscles, decreases stress, strengthens vocal muscles, improves breathing and posture, massages the muscles of the digestive system, boosts the immune system by releasing endorphins and stimulates the whole body, bringing peace and harmony to all levels of being.

When we sing or chant, we are usually unaware of the harmonic nature of the voice, however in certain places such as theatres, places of worship, or our own bathrooms, the voice becomes enhanced and we suddenly become aware of a richer sound, which in turn, has a profound effect on the physical body and the way we feel. When we lift our voices in song a creative power is released.

The ancients were well aware of the power of harmonics and constructed many of their ancient sites with this in mind. In Shamanic traditions, the sound healer developed the ability to create multiple overtones or 'vocal harmonics' by singing two or more notes simultaneously, a technique that was used for invoking the gods and balancing the subtle energy bodies.

Music rich in harmonics, such as Gregorian chanting, Indian classical music or a cappella, can induce a state of altered consciousness and modify our brainwave patterns in order that we become more relaxed and connected.

Chants sung by some Mongolian throat singers, or Tibetan monks, pair together harmonic frequencies that are so deep, they appear to be almost an inhuman growl, with those of much higher frequency overtones, which sound almost angelic.

Through charging the cortex of the brain, this combination of harmonics and overtones brings about profound transformational effects, stimulating health and well-being.

Almost every spiritual tradition on Earth has, or does, incorporate chants or mantras in order to either worship the Divine or to ask for healing. The word 'chant' originates from the Latin word *canere,* meaning 'to sing', whilst the word 'mantra' is a Sanskrit word meaning 'instrument of thought'.

In many orthodox religions, group prayers are recited or chanted by the congregation, whilst other paths may choose a more repetitive mantra or chant to evoke the deities, raise energy, enhance meditation, change consciousness or bring about healing.

Chanting harmonises the right and left sides of the brain, bringing a sense of calm and peace. In addition, it also helps to oxygenate the brain, reduce the heart rate, regularise blood pressure and, as Dr Ranjie Singe discovered during his research, chanting also causes the release of melatonin which aids sleep.

Chants also add another dimension of their own, for the director of The Research Group for Mind-Body Dynamics, Dr David Shananoff-Khalsa, believes that the repetitive nature of a chant or mantra enables the tongue to stimulate the meridians inside the mouth, which again helps to enhance the healing process.

According to Jonathan Goldman, writer, musician, teacher and one of the world's leading authorities on sound healing and a pioneer in the field of harmonics, there are three specific mantras that may be chanted for powerful transformational effects, regardless of the note, pitch or frequency of the voice. These sounds are the powerful: 'OM', 'AH' and 'HU'.

OM

Perhaps the most recognised of all chants is the OM (pronounced 'OM', 'UM', 'UNG', 'ANG', 'ONG' or 'AUM'), a Sanskrit word, which originates from the Hindu tradition and is thought to mean 'God'. It is a sound that is placed at the beginning of most Hindu texts as a sacred incantation before the reading of the Vedas.

It is a sound associated with peace and is also credited with the ability to balance the human energy field and heal the physical body. It is thought by many to be one of the oldest vocal sounds in existence, which has been chanted throughout millennia and is often considered to be the original primordial sound; referred to as the 'mantra of creation'.

AH

This is an extremely powerful sound and one which we associate with love and compassion, hence its ability to resonate with the heart chakra. It is a sacred mantra in many Eastern spiritual traditions and is the sound that can be found in several of the deities names including: Allah, Buddha, Yahweh, Krishna, Tara and Saraswati. The sound is also to be found in certain sacred words such as *Halleluiah* and *Amen*. Many believe that this is the primary sound made when we are born into this world and it is the final sound we make when we breathe our last.

HU

In certain Yogi traditions, and within the mystical Islamic tradition of the Sufi, HU is considered to be the highest vibratory mantra and the most sacred. It is usually pronounced, according to tradition, as 'YOU' or 'WHO' although the Sufis often express it as a buzzing sound which they consider to be good for the throat chakra.

HU is thought to activate the heart and crown chakras and is considered to be the sound that is present within nature, from the buzzing of the bees to the roar of a waterfall. It is also believed to lead the chanter to connect with the Divine essence and thus experience enlightenment.

All three of these mantras can be used together as in the Tibetan Buddhist tradition where it is known as 'The Mantra of Blessing' and is chanted as 'OM AH HU'.

The Healing Power of Words

We are all able to appreciate the profound effect that words can have on our lives, whether in a positive or negative context. Comments, both kind and cruel, can stay with us for a life time, inspiring us to achieve great things or preventing us from ever reaching our true potential.

We affect everyone we come into contact with by the words we choose and should, perhaps, take a moment, especially if we are angry or feeling impatient, before speaking. Harsh words, if taken to heart, remain in the memory and are often the cause of imbalance in the subtle energy fields. Kind words, however, said with love, empathy or understanding, are powerful healing vibrations. Likewise, beautiful poetry or prose spoken aloud can transport us to other worlds and, in so doing, open up vital pathways to healing. In the words of Sarah Fielding:

'The words of kindness are more healing to a drooping heart than balm or honey.'

On occasions, our life experiences become so overwhelming and traumatic that we find ourselves needing professional help in order to re-write the blueprint that has become embedded into our psyche. It is at times like these that we may turn to a practitioner who is adept in one of the 'talking therapies' such as psychotherapy, counselling or hypnotherapy.

The Power of Silence

Everything that is creates a sound vibration, so perhaps the quest to seek absolute silence would perhaps be deemed a futile one.

The closest we can come to achieving silence is to switch off everything that is manmade, remove ourselves from the company of others for a while and immerse ourselves in the peace and tranquillity of nature or a private space at home where we are able to experience relief from our hectic daily schedule. Just ten minutes each day can have tremendous health benefits.

For many of us, though, silence is a frightening prospect. We are unfamiliar with it, for our world is full of noise from the moment we wake to the moment we return to sleep, yet it is only within the silence that the heart beat of creation can be felt.

In silence there is no where to hide, there are no distractions and we are forced to come face to face with our one true nature. How many of us can honestly say we have journeyed within, to the depth of our soul, to the still point of silence, in order to discover who we really are? It is through the practice of meditation and entering the silence that this becomes possible.

Many people shy away from meditation because of its very nature. It is not however a place to fear, but is a place of renewal, a place where we can reconnect with our own core of energy. Silence is tangible and offers anyone who dares to touch it, endless possibilities and potential for transformation.

The more silent we become, the more stillness we are able to experience. Silence eventually brings enlightenment through helping us to realise what is important. It strips away the inflated ego and, in return, offers us inner peace. Silence offers us the truth and through the truth we come to know ourselves.

Dedication

For me the sense of hearing is symbolic of the element of air, for it is through this element that sound waves travel, enabling me to hear the world in which I live.

The sense of hearing enables me to hear the words of others as well as my own voice. It reminds me that I should listen to others and also be aware of what I say.

Sound brings me pleasure through the rush of the wind, the crackle of the fire, the roar of the waves and the heartbeat of the earth. It allows me to hear my husband's lovely Irish accent, the drums in Padstow on May Day morning, the haunting sound of the flute, a seagull's call, the tinkling of wind chimes, words of love and beauty, magickal songs and chants and the virtual silence of Bodmin Moor.

The following dedication over on the next page to the goddess is an example of how we can express our appreciation for our sense of hearing.

Light a yellow candle, symbolic of the solar plexus centre, thought and communication and either, choose a piece of music to play softly in the background, or play an instrument yourself whilst chanting the following dedication:

Lady Goddess, gift bearer of the senses,
I appreciate and honour my sense of hearing.
I give thanks that through hearing I am able to rejoice in the sound of nature.
I give thanks that through hearing I am able to listen to the wisdom and eloquence of others.
I give thanks that through hearing I am able to give and receive healing vibrations.
Please accept this music/song as a token of my gratitude.

Let the candle burn right down if possible. It may be a generous gesture to volunteer to sing, read a poem, or tell a story at a residential home or nursery group. Alternatively, pay someone a compliment or tell a loved one how much you care.

Conclusion

Sound is one of the most transformative energies on the planet. Not only is it capable of destruction on many levels, but it is also capable of bringing great enrichment, feelings of peace and harmony and the possibility of restoring health to the mind, body and spirit

The sounds we choose to surround ourselves with are therefore of the utmost importance and can often make the difference between illness and health. In the words of Plato:

'Music is a moral law. It gives soul to the universe, wings to the mind, flight to the imagination, a charm to sadness, gaiety and life to everything. It is the essence of order, and leads to all that is good, just, and beautiful, of which it is the invisible, but nevertheless dazzling, passionate and eternal form.'

Mrs Darley Tale: The Drum

'Ah, here she is look.' Mrs Darley waved as I approached the cottages just as dusk was gathering one late June evening. 'Now you can ask her yourself.'

'Ask me what?' I smiled as Rose appeared from behind Mrs Darley.

'Would you like to come to a drumming workshop?' she asked, 'next Tuesday night down at the school? The parents and teachers association have had it arranged for ages, but unfortunately, with this chicken pox epidemic, lots of people have pulled out so they've opened it up to the general public.'

'Well I don't really have a very good sense of rhythm,' I began.

'Good,' said Mrs Darley, 'because it's a beginners workshop so there's no need for any experience and, perhaps after some instruction, we can all drum in the summer solstice this year with a little bit of rhythm!'

With my argument shot down in flames, the following Tuesday found me sitting in the school hall with an expectant dgembe before me, which I discovered during the course of the evening, was an African tribal drum, used for the purpose of ritual ceremonies and, much to my surprise, healing. The initial apprehension I felt as the evening began gradually dissolved into what I can only describe as a partial trance-like state as our hypnotic rhythms filled the room.

'Wow,' I said as we were making our way onto the car park, 'that was incredible! I feel … well, different somehow and I had no idea that drumming could be used for healing purposes.'

'Oh yes, dear,' said Mrs Darley, 'sound has been used in healing rituals for thousands of years by different cultures all over the world.'

'Oooo, I wonder if Bod could be persuaded to tell us the story of his Great Uncle Joe,' mused Rose as we got into the car, 'it's a strange tale about drums and things, although I haven't heard him tell it for years so my memories are a bit vague.'

'That would be most interesting,' said Mrs Darley, 'especially as I was hoping you would all join me for a light supper when we get back home. So, whilst I put the final touches to it, you, Lucy, dear, can go and fetch your Dad.'

Needless to say, we all eagerly accepted Mrs Darley's invitation and within half an hour Bod, Rose, Lucy and I found ourselves sitting in Mrs Darley's cottage with a plate of delicious smoked salmon and salad.

'So you all enjoyed your drumming session then?' asked Bod.

'Mmmm, it was really good, in fact, I think it might be something I'd like to look into further,' said Rose.

'And what was it about the drumming that so moved you?' asked Mrs Darley.

'Well, I feel different … clearer somehow, if that makes sense,' said Rose.

'I know just what you mean,' I said, 'I feel the same.'

'Well sound can have a profound effect on all levels of our being,' said Bod, 'a fact that my Great Uncle Joe testified to on many an occasion before he died.'

'Ah,' said Mrs Darley, 'Rose mentioned that you might be persuaded to share the story of your Great Uncle with us all.'

'Well,' began Bod, 'Uncle Joe had spent most of his life sailing the seas, rather like me I suppose and, when he finally retired, he had great trouble in settling into a daily routine on dry land. In fact so much so that he actually began to pine for the life he once knew and he spent hours just sitting on the harbour wall staring out to sea. Eventually he became ill, a fact that my grandmother put down to him not fulfilling his heartfelt desires and wishes. What he suffered from, though, wasn't what you might call a 'normal' disease, but was a list of most peculiar complaints, which no doctor seemed to be able to diagnose let alone cure.'

'Like what?' Rose asked.

'Well, inexplicable symptoms really I suppose,' Bod said thoughtfully, 'Great Aunt Beth used to say that sometimes he was tired to the point of exhaustion, yet had disturbed sleep and that he suffered from bouts of severe depression accompanied by painful muscles and joints. I suppose we might call it ME or, these days, chronic fatigue, but back in Uncle Joe's time there was no explanation and so he just had to suffer the symptoms.

'Now at this time he lived down on the south Cornish coast and being unable to sleep one warm summer's night, he decided to walk down through the village to the shore, in the hopes that the sea would calm his thoughts and refresh his aching legs.

'When he arrived at the harbour, the tide was well out and there was a full moon hanging in the sky. He made his way down the harbour steps onto the beach and began to walk out towards the headland just as he had done hundreds of times before. As he passed the familiar cave, which was a well known storage place for smuggled goods in the old days, he became aware of the sound of drumming coming from deep inside.

'He stopped just outside to listen and, after a few minutes, decided to venture in. Once inside, the sound of the drums became much louder and reverberated around the dark cavern, filling every inch of space with their hypnotic rhythm. He totally lost all track of time and it was only when the drumming finally stopped that he came back to the real world once again and made moves to leave before he was discovered.

'Uncle Joe returned home to his bed and awoke several hours later only to find a distinct improvement in his pain levels and so, in order to ensure that this was not merely coincidence, he decided to revisit the cave that night just as he had done the previous evening.

'As darkness fell, Uncle Joe once again made his way along the beach to the cave, but to his disappointment, the cave was silent and so on he walked to the water's edge where he began to bathe his aching legs. After standing for a while in the shallows, he began to make his way back up the beach, but as he neared the cave, he felt his heart thump with excitement, for once more he could hear the familiar beat of the drums.

'Again, he stepped inside the cave and stood, letting the drums weave their magick in, around and through every part of his very being, allowing himself to become one with the rhythm.

'All at once, just as it had the previous evening, the music stopped and he found himself plunging back into the real world, yet re-entering it with a renewed sense of both hope and well-being.

'On this occasion, however, his curiosity overcame his fear of discovery and he began to edge his way further into the tangible darkness of the cave. He could make out the sound of dripping water as the space narrowed and soon found himself unable to progress any further as his hand touched the hard, cold rock which heralded the back of the cave.

'Where were the drummers? No one had passed him as he stood listening. His hands explored the slimy wetness of the rock, hoping to find a further passage but his searching was in vain.

'The following morning, for the first time in years, he rose from his bed without pain or exhaustion and decided there and then to re-visit the cave, in the hope that daylight would help him to discover a hidden passageway and also because he wished to leave a gift.'

'Why?' asked Lucy.

'Well, Luce, he wanted to leave a token of thanks to whoever or whatever had caused, what he considered to be, nothing short of a miraculous healing. He was, after all, an old seafarer and superstition dictates that you should never take from the sea gods without giving something in return.

'Half an hour later he found himself back at the cave with his offering of a beautiful conch shell, given to him many years previously by someone in the Caribbean who had told him it was a good luck charm which would always keep him safe.'

'Why did he give it away then?' asked Lucy.

'Because it meant something to him,' Bod replied.

'But why would you give something away that you liked?' Lucy persisted.

'Perhaps I can offer an explanation,' said Mrs Darley.

Bod nodded.

'When we make an offering or a sacrifice to the gods in return for a gift, we must give something that either comes from the heart, such as something we have made ourselves, or, which has real meaning for us, otherwise it is not a true token of thanks.' said Mrs Darley.

'It would be easy to go out and buy flowers or some other token of thanksgiving, but your Great, Great Uncle Joe gave away something to which he had a strong emotional attachment and therefore it became a heartfelt token of thanks and one that the gods would have appreciated'

We all remained in quiet contemplation for a moment until Rose broke the silence.

'So while in the cave did he find a secret passage?'

Bod shook his head. 'No he didn't, however that's not quite the end of the story.'

'Why?' asked Lucy, 'what happened?'

'Well,' said Bod, 'when he arrived home, Great Aunt Beth was waiting for him by the gate. "I didn't know you'd taken up music," she said.

'"I haven't," he replied.

'"Well someone's just delivered a drum," she said. "I found it leaning up against the front door".'

'Oh, my goodness,' said Rose. 'Did he ever find out who it was? Was there a message with it?'

Bod shook his head. 'No. It remained an unsolved mystery right up until his death some twenty years later.'

'Is the drum still in your family?' I asked.

'Sadly I don't know,' said Bod, 'I'm afraid my cousins both moved abroad and I haven't heard from them for years.'

Mrs Darley leaned forward in her chair. 'It matters not, my dears, whether the drum still exists. What we can all take from this fascinating story is that sound does indeed have the power to heal. What we must remember, however, is that it is not just the loudest or most tuneful sounds which have the ability to impart this precious vibrational gift, but that kind words carried on the breath of the human voice are also capable of healing the human soul.'

Sound

Kind words softly spoken lift my spirit,
Sweet flutes gently played release my mind.

Ringing, chiming, toning, humming,
Chanting, rhyming, singing, drumming.

Rhythmic chants revive and heal my body,
Hypnotic drums restore and raise my soul.

Ringing, chiming, toning, humming,
Chanting, rhyming, singing, drumming.

Chapter 8

The Sense of Sight

The Colour of Day
Finger blushes brush the break of dawn,
Softening, quietening the rising of the light.
Apricot clouds part, heads bowed in reverence
Against the brilliance of the sun.

Daylight bursts upon the canvas of life,
Illuminating History's Creation.
Green eyes of envy covet and yearn
Beneath the orange flame of day.

Scarlett shadows speed the dying sun.
Darkness unfurls from magenta ribbons
Strewn within the violet hush of night.
All is at peace before the blue breath of day.

Mrs Darley Tale: Seeing the Truth

It was Lucy's birthday and, as a surprise, Bod had organised a trip in a pony and trap courtesy of Mia's son-in-law Joe. The plan was that as soon as we had waved off Rose, Bod, Lucy and a couple of her friends, Mrs Darley, Peter, Phyllis, Eddie and I would pack Eddie's old Land Rover with a pre-prepared picnic and drive over to Gold Diggings Quarry in order that we would have everything set out by the time the trap arrived.

Gold Diggings was once a working quarry, way out

across Caradon Moor on the western side of the Cheesewring and had been flooded at the end of its life as a haven for wildlife. To me, however, it had an air of eerie silence and even on a beautiful day it always gave me the impression that it was watching and waiting. It reminded me of the clashing rocks in the film of *Jason and the Argonauts* where, apart from the creak of the oars, the silence became almost tangible before the rocks unleashed their fury.

On this beautiful August afternoon, however, even I had to admit that the faint wisps of cirrus clouds mirrored in the deep waters of the quarry were quite beautiful. We found a flat boulder of rock in a sheltered spot and had just arranged the picnic when Phyllis called, 'Here they come! And it looks as though there's another trap following behind.'

We all stood in order to see who else was joining us and, as they came nearer, I felt my heart quicken as I saw Mia accompanied by the softly spoken Irishman who had read my fortune in the flames of the fire the previous summer.

'I hope you don't mind us gate crashing your party,' Mia smiled as she was helped down from the trap by Peter, 'but Bod and Rose said it would be alright and as it was such a lovely day we thought it was an ideal opportunity to bring both of the ponies out, so Niga and Joe took the birthday girl and Tad and I followed behind.'

My head was suddenly swirling, so Tad wasn't with Niga as I had mistakenly assumed the previous summer.

'It's always lovely to see you, Mia,' said Mrs Darley, embracing her in a warm hug and immediately bringing my thoughts back to the moment at hand. 'There's more than enough food for everyone. Come now, let's drink a toast to Lucy and eat before the food spoils.'

With the food eaten and the cake cut, Lucy and her friends disappeared to see the ponies, leaving the adults alone to make their own amusement, at which point the subject meandered to that of favourite authors.

I listened as Tolstoy, Dickens and Zola all made their way into the conversation and achieved oh's and ah's of approval as some of their highly prized achievements were discussed.

Niga, whom I had never heard speak before, was particularly animated, telling us that she was an avid reader who loved the more contemporary writers and that the measure of a good writer was whether they had the ability to stir the emotions.

'I agree absolutely,' Phyllis nodded, 'that's exactly what you want when you read a book; the ability to be moved.'

'And what about you?' Tad suddenly turned his attention towards me, 'which author stirs your emotions?'

I felt myself redden as all eyes turned to me and wondered whether my suggestion would meet with approval, or whether my choice was too predictable.

'Daphne Du Maurier,' I said.

'Which book particularly?' Phyllis asked.

'Oh, it's hard to just choose one,' I said, '*The House on the Strand*, *Jamaica Inn*, *The Scapegoat*, *Rebecca*, they all have their own air of mystery and suspense.'

'And what about *French Man's Creek*?' smiled Mia, does that feature in your list of favourites?'

'Oh, yes,' I said, 'I love that one too.'

'Mmmm, but in reality it's just a soppy Cornish love story with swashbuckling pirates and do or dare adventure,' interjected Niga, 'all a bit old hat now. Perhaps you should try something new, drag your reading into the twentieth century. I'll lend you a few easy read contemporary authors when we get back.'

Although I thanked her, I immediately allowed myself to feel belittled at my literary choice and my burning cheeks betrayed my embarrassment to the assembled company.

'Well I've always been a fan of Daphne,' said Eddie, 'and like you say, she's got the ability to weave a certain amount of suspense into all of her stories, which always keeps you on edge.'

I smiled at him, grateful for his support and, in order to divert attention away from my choice of author, I began to clear away the remains of the food before taking them over to the trap.

The sun was beginning to go down as I turned away from making a fuss of the ponies and I decided to take a walk over to the high part of the quarry in order to get a good view of the evening sky.

I climbed up over the rocks and sat for a while with my arms wrapped around my knees, watching the shadows lengthen.

Feeling decidedly chilled after a while and thinking that I had been away from the party for far too long, I stood and began to pick my way over the uneven rocks.

It was at this point that I became aware of voices and, as I looked down, I saw Tad and Niga standing below me in what can only be described as a rather intimate position. My disappointment was immediate and instantly I turned away, in order to find another route of descent away from their view.

As I jumped down onto the grassy bank of the moor, my blind panic of escapism led me to bump into someone coming the other way.

'Oh, I'm sorry,' I called out as firm arms reached out to steady me.

'Are you alright, dear? I was just coming to find you,' the reassuring voice of Mrs Darley steadied my jangling nerves.

'Yes, yes I'm fine,' I said smiling a little too brightly.

'He's not your pirate,' she said gently.

'Who?' I asked.

'Tad,' she said. 'I know, my dear, that I often suggest your life is devoid of interaction with the opposite sex, but he's not the one for you. His destiny and yours do not lie together.'

I turned away from her, grateful to the gathering dusk for hiding my embarrassment, 'I don't know what you mean.'

'Oh, I think you do. I saw the way you looked at him. In fact, over the years I've seen the way many women have looked at him, but Tad is a born traveller. Every summer he makes his way into Cornwall and stays in the local vicinity. Niga, Mia's daughter, befriended him many years ago in her youth and it was through him that she met her husband, Joe, but I know Tad of old, his Irish charm and good looks make a lethal combination for many an unsuspecting woman.'

'I wouldn't have put Niga in the category of an unsuspecting woman,' I said.

'Wouldn't you?' she asked.

I shook my head. 'No, I would have thought that she would be quite capable of knowing what she was getting herself into.'

'Well, let's just say that it's not always those who shout loudest that have the most insight. Sometimes, my dear, we see things that perhaps we wish we hadn't and yet those visions can often turn out to be our saviour. Come,' she said, taking my arm, 'it's time to make our way home.'

Introducing the Sense of Sight

Sight is thought to be the last sense to develop in an unborn baby, albeit it is quite difficult to assess whilst still in the womb. In babies that are born some thirty-one to thirty-two weeks prematurely it has been noted, however, that they are able to see a distance of between eight to twelve inches.

Sight is considered by many to be the most valuable of all the senses. Growing up with both a cousin who lost his sight at the age of five and watching the deterioration of my mother's sight, due to glaucoma, has certainly given me a strong appreciation of this precious sense.

From the moment we wake until the moment we fall asleep, we look at the world around us and make judgments based on what we see. Very often however we allow what we see to dominate our other senses and we are liable to become easily seduced by an attractive face, the owner of which may turn out in reality not to be quite as nice as we had hoped, or perhaps become tempted by the fancy car which takes all of our money filling it with petrol.

We are also capable of only seeing what we want to see, as the well known experiment of a ball game illustrates. Here a clip is shown of six people passing a ball to one another and the viewer is asked to count the passes. When the film is played back it is astonishing to see that a man in a hairy gorilla suit actually walked straight through the group of players, but so intent is the viewer on counting the passes that the gorilla is not seen.

Nevertheless, the gift of sight is one that the majority of us would wish to preserve for as long as possible and is a valuable medium through which we are able to heal. Healing through this sense may be instigated through looking at shapes and images which bring us pleasure, such as a piece of art or a beautiful face or, perhaps, the one which this chapter sets out to explore, the healing vibrations of the visible electromagnetic spectrum - colour.

Understanding the Sense of Sight

In order to perceive the beauty of the world around us we are blessed with a pair of highly tuned organs, namely the eyes, which allow us to see form, the full colour spectrum and all the colours in between.

The eyes are almost spherical in shape and lie in the cone shaped orbit of the skull, protected by the eyelids at the front and a pad of fat behind. The eyeballs, meanwhile, are attached to the skull by six small muscles that move the eyes in all directions.

The eye itself has a jelly like centre and is covered by three layers:

1. The Fibrous Tunic

This is the outermost tough fibrous layer, which protects the eye and maintains its shape. It consists of the *sclera*, which is the white of the eye and the *cornea*, which transmits and refracts light.

2. The Vascular Tunic

This is the middle layer, which is dark brown and prevents the rays of light which have entered the eye, from being reflected back out. It consists of the *choroid* that supplies blood vessels to the eye and the *ciliary* that supports the lens and secretes a watery fluid called the *aqueous humour*. This, in turn, provides nutrients for the lens and helps to maintain pressure in the front of the eye.

3. The Internal Tunic

This is the inner layer that contains the retina, which consists of a network of nerve cells, fibres and light sensitive cells called 'rods' and 'cones'. The 120 million rods are light sensitive and primarily concerned with image. These allow us to see shapes and form, becoming more active when the light fades and we are unable to perceive colour.

The sixty three million cones respond to the whole colour range of the visible electromagnetic spectrum and are most active during the day when the presence of light enables us to perceive colour. The marriage of rods and cones therefore literally allows us to see 'the full picture'.

The visual field is the part of the external world, which is projected onto the retina. The cornea and the lens focus the right part of the visual field onto the left part of the retina, whilst the left part of the visual field is focussed onto the right part of the retina. Within each eye the visual field is projected upside down and then reversed, a process known as refraction.

This visual data is then sent via the optic nerve to the visual cortex at the back of the brain, which stimulates the hypothalamus, pituitary and pineal glands all of which, respond to messages received from other parts of the body about the quantity and colour quality of light shining into the body. In this way we are able to perceive accurately what the body experiences. For example when we walk out into the sunshine on a beautiful day, we see that it is beautiful and we feel its warmth, but because our brain simultaneously gathers information from our sense of touch and sight, the one sensation supports and confirms the other.

The History of Colour in Healing

Although shape and image can bring us pleasure and, in so doing, enable us to release the 'feel good hormones' called *endorphins* into the bloodstream, these things are quite subjective and as such are difficult to form into a so-called therapy. Colour, however, is something that has a profound effect on us all regardless of whether we realise it or not and, as such, has been used as a healing modality for over 4,000 years.

The ancient Egyptians outlined a list of coloured cures on a papyrus dating back some 3,550 years. One cure suggested taking a combination of red lead, black lizards and verdigris (green copper salt), which were to be mixed with beetle wax in order to treat cataracts.

It is also known that the Egyptians built temples especially for the purpose of colour healing. Here the patient would lie down as the sun shone on them through coloured gem stones such as rubies, sapphires and emeralds, each of which would carry their own unique healing vibration.

In the *Nei/ching*, a Chinese medical text compiled almost 2,000 years ago, colour diagnosis is mentioned: 'When the viscera are green like kingfishers wings then they are filled with life, when their colour is green like grass they are without life.'

It is thanks to these early civilizations that precious information with regards to the healing properties of colour has been preserved, for although the Greeks such as Pythagoras, Plato and Aristotle had an interest in colour, they were more interested in the science of colour rather than its healing properties.

Around 1000AD, Avicenna, the great physician and author of *The Canon of Medicine*, considered colour to be of vital importance in the diagnosis and treatment of disease and developed a chart that related colour to the temperature and physical condition of the body. His view was that red moved the blood, blue or white cooled it and yellow reduced muscular pain and inflammation.

During the Middle Ages, Paracelsus reintroduced these important colour healing philosophies along with those of music and herbs. Sadly, Paracelsus was ridiculed throughout Europe for his pioneering work, which resulted in most of his valuable manuscripts being burned. This dramatic action led the tide to turn once again towards the scientific nature of colour and its analysis, an explanation for which was finally pioneered by Sir Isaac Newton during the seventeenth century.

In 1876, Augustus Pleasanton, an American civil war general, conducted his own experiments involving colour, eventually publishing his book *The Influence of the Blue Ray of the Sunlight and of the Blue Colour of the Sky,* in which he explained how the colour blue is capable of improving the health of crops and improving the health of humans.

During the twentieth century, many investigations on the therapeutic uses of colour were carried out by the Austrian philosopher Rudolf Steiner, who related colour to form shape and sound and considered certain combinations of colour and shape to have either destructive or regenerative effects on living organisms.

Steiner's work was continued by the renowned colour therapist Theo Gimbel, who also explored the claims of Max Luscher, a Swiss psychotherapist. Luscher stated that colour preferences were capable of disclosing a person as they truly were rather than who they perceived themselves to be. Luscher invented the *Luscher Colour Test*, which involved placing eight coloured cards on a table and asking a client to list them in order of colour preference, without conscious deliberation.

The test was then repeated, although the cards were placed in different positions on the table to begin with and a personality assessment was then made based upon these two tests. The results and stressors highlighted in the client's life would then be treated using verbal therapies or homeopathic remedies.

Today colour is recognised as a healing therapy in its own right and many therapists impart colour vibrations to their clients via coloured lights and lasers. The healing energies of colour however, are something that each of us can incorporate into our lives on a daily basis.

The Science of Colour

Colour forms part of the natural energy of the universe from the spectacular sight of a rainbow to the beauty of a summer garden and, as such, affects our lives on many levels. Even our language can be described as colourful, for we use such expressions as: feeling blue, seeing red and turning green with envy, but what exactly is colour?

In the mid-sixth century BC, Pythagoras believed that all objects gave off light particles which made them appear coloured and visible to the human eye, whilst Plato, some 150 years later, believed that the eye emitted a light that bounced off objects, allowing the eye to determine shape and colour.

Aristotle, almost a century later, however, was not in agreement with these earlier philosophers and put forward the theory that light travelled in waves rather than particles, a debate that continued until the mid-seventeenth century.

In 1665 Sir Isaac Newton realised that although sunlight appeared to be white, it was in fact a blend of coloured light and sought to prove his theory by passing sunlight through a prism. This resulted in the appearance of a rainbow of coloured light or what we now term 'the full colour spectrum' or 'rainbow effect'.

Newton concluded that each of the seven colours present in a rainbow (where sunlight is refracted through a raindrop) had a different wavelength and frequency, with red having the longest and lowest frequency and violet having the shortest and highest.

Newton's theories were expanded upon during the late nineteenth and early twentieth centuries by the likes of the physicists Lenard, Planck and Einstein, who, through the use of quantum physics, proved that light comprised of small packets of energy called *quanta*.

Einstein went on to formulate *quantum*[3] *theory* (also known as quantum mechanics or quantum physics), which accepted elements of both the particle and wave theories.

These quanta, Einstein referred to as *photons*, which he discovered moved in wave-like forms and concluded that all forms of matter are simply light waves in motion, from the longest and lowest to the shortest and highest.

When arranged in wavelength and frequency order this produced what we refer to today as the 'electromagnetic spectrum', of which the full colour spectrum forms a tiny, but visible part as illustrated in Table 2.0, over on the next page.

Since quantum mechanics has become more popular, it has branched out into many associated realms, viz: quantum chemistry, quantum electronics, quantum optics and quantum information science.

---

[3] The word *quantum* derives from Latin, meaning 'how great' or 'how much'.

The Electromagnetic Spectrum

Shortest wavelength	**Longest wavelength**
Highest frequency	**Lowest frequency**
Most energy	**Least energy**

Cosmic Rays/ Gamma/ X-Rays/ Ultraviolet/ Visible/ Infrared/ Microwaves/ Radar/ FM/ TV/ AM
Light

||

Violet/Indigo/Blue/Green/Yellow/Orange/Red

|| ||

380 nanometres **Wavelength** **760 nanometres**

Table 2.0

The Effect of Colour in our Daily Lives

We are influenced and, to some extent, manipulated by colour on a daily basis, with design and marketing consultants being very aware of its importance in their promotional and packaging material.

Thousands of pounds have been spent delving into our psyches to uncover what will influence us to buy certain products. We buy more toiletries and medical supplies when they are packaged in pure, clean, cool colours such as white, blue and green, whilst energy foods and drinks are packaged in more vibrant colours such as red, orange and yellow. Throughout our lives, these colour expectations enter our psyche and we instinctively know what type of product we are looking at simply by its colour.

Outside the advertising industry, however, experiments have been carried out to illustrate the power of colour on human behaviour. In an American prison for violent offenders, each cell was painted a different colour. The inhabitants of the cells painted in the colour 'Baker Miller Pink' showed a marked improvement in their levels of violence and aggression, resulting in the other cells being painted the same colour.

In experiments concerning young children, it has been noted that when a black or white board is surrounded by red, orange or yellow, children have a longer attention span.

Theo Gimbel, author of *Healing Through Colour,* discovered that the quality and intensity of light changes every two hours throughout the day, a fact he claimed has a dramatic effect on our behaviour, emotions and physical energy levels as illustrated in Table 2.1.

Time	Colour	Energy Level
24.00	Magenta	Slow
01.00	Magenta	Slow
02.00	Purple	Slow
03.00	Purple	Fast
04.00	Violet	Fast
05.00	Violet	Fast
06.00	Blue	Fast
07.00	Blue	Fast
08.00	Turquoise	Fast
09.00	Turquoise	Slow
10.00	Peacock Green	Slow
11.00	Peacock Green	Slow
12.00	Green	Slow
13.00	Green	Slow
14.00	Apple Green	Slow
15.00	Apple Green	Fast
16.00	Yellow	Fast

17.00	Yellow	Fast
18.00	Orange	Fast
19.00	Orange	Fast
20.00	Red	Fast
21.00	Red	Slow
22.00	Mauve	Slow
23.00	Mauve	Slow

Table 2.1

Daylight contains the full spectrum of the visible electromagnetic field, which is why natural daylight is healing both to mind and body. It also explains why many people suffer from SAD (seasonal affective disorder), often becoming depressed and withdrawn during the winter months when daylight hours are at a minimum. Natural spectrum lamps are now accepted as a medical treatment for those suffering from SAD, compensating the body for a lack of natural light. Apart from natural daylight, we are also affected by the colours we live with and the colours we both wear and consume through our food choices.

Décor

The colour of our décor has a marked effect upon the psyche, for our bodies are continually absorbing the vibration of the chosen colour scheme.

Apart from affecting our physical health, colour vibrations also alter our perception of temperature within a room. Reds, oranges and yellows make a room feel warmer and are more stimulating, whilst greens, blues and violets have the opposite effect, inducing a cooler and more relaxing atmosphere.

Although red is often described as the colour of passion, it is advisable to avoid red in the bedroom as its stimulating vibrations are capable of affecting sleep patterns, therefore blue would be a more relaxing choice. Likewise, attempting to concentrate in a blue office is not recommended as we may feel too relaxed or lethargic. Yellow would be a better choice in order that the mind is stimulated.

Wardrobe

Our wardrobe is a key indicator of the colours we need in our lives at specific times and many of us tend to go through phases of liking certain colours according to where we are in our life cycle and how we feel. Individual colours are explored in more detail later in this chapter.

Food

Eating foods of various colours ensures that we have both a healthy diet and that we benefit from the colour vibrations given off by those foods. The prettier the content of plate, the healthier the meal.

Exploring Colour Healing

Colour therapy, or *chromotherapy* to give it its correct name, works at the level of the subtle energy field, bringing any energy disturbances back into balance through the use of the correct colour vibration, thereby affecting every level of our being. In Theo Gimbel's words:

'We respond to colour through the heart (intuition, emotion), the mind (brain, intellect), the body and its senses.'

In colour healing, the colours vary to those of the traditional seven chakras (see chapter two) and consist of eight colours. These eight colours reflect the changing light that takes place over a twenty four hour period and include: red, orange, yellow, green, turquoise, blue, violet, magenta and shades thereof.

Turquoise, although not having jurisdiction over one of the major chakras, governs the minor thymus chakra and plays an important role in the building of the immune system.

Magenta, meanwhile, governs the little known eighth chakra, which sits in the auric field just above the crown centre and is the energy centre through which the soul is thought to leave at the point of physical death.

For the purpose of colour healing, indigo, which traditionally governs the brow chakra or third eye, is omitted and amalgamated with the crown chakra, which vibrates in harmony with the colour violet.

The decision as to which colour is needed by an individual at any one time can be ascertained by a colour therapist through a variety of methods including muscle testing (kinesiology), pendulum dowsing, Kirlian photography and the more complex method of sensing colours in the spine as devised by Theo Gimbel.

As with any modality of complementary therapy, ideas and thoughts vary. Many colour therapists choose to work with form as well as colour and consider the marrying of the two to not only utilise both the rods and cones of the eyes, but also to harmonise the left and right hand side of the brain.

Some colour therapists will opt to work only with the colours they have diagnosed as being needed, whilst other therapists will combine the indicated colour with its complementary colour.

Treatment may include any of the following depending on the therapist's choice:

- Coloured silks
- Crystals
- Coloured laser lights
- Sunlight
- Coloured foods
- Coloured clothes
- Rainbow water (exposed to sunlight)
- Colour breathing
- White light shone through coloured filters
- Suggestions on changing home décor
- Crystal or glass prisms
- Coloured baths
- Coloured eye lenses

Many of us may not be able to locate a colour therapist in our locality, but there is little to prevent us from bringing the healing power of colour into our lives through our décor, the clothes we wear, the food we eat or by carrying a coloured object such as a crystal, as discussed below. (Complementary colours are given in brackets).

If you are concerned about a particular medical problem, please consult your GP in the first instance.

Red (Turquoise)

The colour red invites us to act on impulse, be spontaneous, passionate and heightens our mood for adventure. It calls us to live life to the full, to take a risk, to lead rather than to follow and to put maximum effort into everything we do.

Red is the colour of the tribal chakra and is recommended when we are looking for inspiration, have a need to dissolve anger, let go of the past, make changes in our lives or would like to imbue our thoughts with positive energy.

In conjunction with turquoise, the colour red helps to counteract infections. Red helps to increase the blood supply to any given area which will deal with any invading bacteria, whilst turquoise will assist in cleansing and reducing inflammation.

The colour red possesses healing vibrations that can assist with the following disorders:

Blood disorders / Anxiety states / Low Blood pressure / Sexual problems / Lethargy / Tiredness / Circulatory dysfunction

Suggested ways of bringing red energy into the auric field include carrying crystals of:

Garnet / Ruby / Haematite

Eating red foods including:

Tomatoes / Red Peppers / Strawberries / Radishes / Red berries

Orange (Blue)

The colour orange brings joy and sunshine into our lives and into the lives of those we come into contact with. It helps to build bridges in times of troubled relationships, encourages us to trust our thoughts, follow our own path and be creative.

Orange is the colour of the sacral chakra and is recommended when we need guidance, particularly when we are undergoing a transition in our lives such as that of childbirth or bereavement.

The colour orange possesses healing vibrations that

can assist with the following disorders:

Depressive states / Kidney disorders / Urinary disorders/ Catarrh / Chest complaints / Low blood pressure / Muscular spasms

Suggested ways of bringing orange energy into the auric field include carrying crystals of:

Carnelian / Moonstone

Eating orange foods including:

Carrots /Oranges /Nectarines / Squash / Orange pepper / Mango

Yellow (Violet)

The colour yellow is the most highly reflective of all the colours and brings a sense of optimism even in the direst of circumstances. It is the colour of the mind and intellect and enables us to have clarity of thought and open up channels of communication, often persuading others to appreciate different points of view.

Yellow is the colour of the solar plexus chakra and is recommended when embarking upon a new form of education or in general need of confidence or enlightenment in order to enable us to enjoy and appreciate all the gifts of being human.

Yellow brings joy and laughter into our world making negativity a thing of the past.

The colour yellow possesses healing vibrations that can assist with the following disorders:

Obsessional thoughts / Negative outlook / Skin disorders / Rheumatism Arthritis / Weakness of motor nerves / Nervous complaints

Suggested ways of bringing yellow energy into the auric field include carrying crystals of:

Citrine / Calcite / Tiger's Eye

Eating yellow foods including:

Banana / Yellow peppers / Lemons / Sweet corn / Cheese / Eggs

Green / Pink (Magenta)

The colour green brings a sense of balance and harmony, helping to promote feelings of peace. It encourages us to be fair in our judgments and to treat others in the way we would like to be treated. Pink, meanwhile, is the colour of love.

Green and pink are the colours of the heart chakra and are recommended when we are in need of physical healing or if we are in the business of healing others and sometimes feel that we would like a helping hand. These colours are particularly helpful when emotional healing is a priority as it brings peace to a troubled heart and brings into our awareness the gift of unconditional love.

The colours of green and pink possess healing vibrations that can assist with the following disorders:

Circulatory disorders / Emotional issues including grief and heartache

Suggested ways of bringing green or pink energy into the auric field include carrying crystals of:

Malachite / Aventurine / Jade / Rose quartz

Eating green and pink foods including:

Leafy green vegetables / Peas / Kiwi / Apples /Green Peppers / Lettuce / Pink grapefruit

Turquoise (Red)

The colour turquoise increases our sensitivity to others and, in so doing, fills those we come into contact with feelings of trust. Turquoise helps us to express ourselves easily and clearly and allows us to become at peace with ourselves.

Turquoise energy sits between the heart and throat chakras and although it does not have jurisdiction over any one of the seven main energy centres, it does govern the lesser known thymus chakra, which is responsible for the overall health of our immune system.

Turquoise enables us to express who we truly are, regardless of the reaction of those around us.

The colour turquoise possesses healing vibrations that can assist with the following disorders:

Infection / Inflammation / Septic conditions / Lymphatic disorders / Nervous tension / Weak immune system / Toxic overload

Suggested ways of bringing turquoise energy into the auric field include carrying crystals of:

Chrysocolla / Turquoise

Blue (Orange)

The colour blue brings a sense of integrity and honesty to all of our dealings and relationships. It helps us to speak out and find our voice albeit in a diplomatic way. It encourages an orderly mind that is both logical and analytical, enabling sound judgments to be made. Blue brings a sense of inner calm and a willingness to give help to others.

Blue is the colour of the throat chakra. It offers protection, helps us to search for our higher truth and provides us with the focus needed to overcome obstacles and become successful.

The colour blue possesses healing vibrations that can assist with the following disorders:

Fear / Tension / Palpitations / Insomnia / Inflammation / Throat disorders / Asthma / Migraine

Suggested ways of bringing blue energy into the auric field include carrying crystals of:

Blue Lace Agate / Sodalite / Lapis Lazuli

Eating blue foods:

Blueberries

Violet (Yellow)

The colour violet opens up the imagination and helps us to become receptive to the ideas of others. It assists us in finding our true spiritual path and helps us to connect with the divine essence. It is a colour which offers serenity and helps us to bring our psychic gifts to the fore.

Violet is the colour of the crown chakra and is recommended in times of self transformation and spiritual growth or when we need to exercise forgiveness or compassion.

The colour violet possesses healing vibrations that can assist with the following disorders:

Low self esteem / Lack of self-respect / Self-abuse / Despair / Low energy levels / nervous system disorders

Suggested ways of bringing violet energy into the auric field include carrying crystals of:

Amethyst / Fluorite

Eating Violet foods:

Aubergine / Black grapes / Plums / Purple sprouting

Magenta (Green)

The colour magenta offers us self-assuredness, allowing us to feel as though we have found our place in the world. It encourages us to step outside of our comfort zone and gives us the confidence to trust our own intuition and know that this alone is the only voice we should listen to.

Magenta energy sits above the crown chakra and although it does not have jurisdiction over any one of the seven main energy centres it does govern the little known eighth chakra, the centre through which our soul energy passes as we leave this earth plane.

Magenta has the ability to teach us about truth, illusion, life and death in order to help us transcend our fears and strengthen the soul. It is indicated in times of grief and when in need of comfort and strength.

The colour magenta possesses healing vibrations that can assist with the following disorders:

Restrictive thought patterns / Refusal to accept circumstances / Feeling stuck

Suggested ways of bringing magenta energy into the auric field includes carrying crystals of:

Magenta agate

Eating magenta foods:

Red cabbage / cherries

The whole body is capable of absorbing light waves; therefore colour does not have to be seen to be of benefit. Colour can be sensed by those who live without the gift of sight and can benefit them in the same way as a sighted person.

As already touched upon earlier in this book, the sense of touch in some blind people is heightened to such a degree that they are actually able to feel whether a colour is warm (red, orange, yellow), neutral (green) or cool (blue, indigo or violet).

The 'Third Eye' and the Power of Visualization

Our 'third eye' assumes the same position as the brow chakra and is often referred to as the 'gateway to the inner realms', or higher consciousness, through which we are able to reach a state of enlightenment. It is also associated with visions, clairvoyance and the ability to see the subtle energy bodies. People who have 'opened' their third eye are often referred to as 'seers', as their sight extends far beyond the limitations of this physical world.

In our normal daily lives, we spend much of our time

thinking, imagining and visualising. We 'see' things in our mind's eye, a phenomenon that is often as powerful as seeing images with our physical eyes.

Many of us are familiar with the concept of 'the power of attraction', where through positive thought and visualization, we are able to attract what we think we need into our lives, including good health. There are numerous studies which illustrate how ill health can be overcome with the help of visualization and many people have healed themselves of various life threatening diseases.

Cancer cells have been 'blasted' out by visualized hoses, 'popped' out of existence by imaginary bubble wrap, or 'rubbed' out with a virtual eraser, all of which are a testament to the power of visualization. 'Seeing' ourselves in our mind's eye in a loving relationship, in a state of happiness, or enjoying good health is as powerful as actually being there in a physical sense, for the mind is unable to distinguish between what is real and what is imagined. Therefore the more we visualize how we would like our lives to be, the more possibility there is of that life manifesting. The ability to visualize is one of the first skills to master in the practice of magick.

We can also use the power of visualization to bring healing colour vibrations into our lives. Colour breathing through the chakras is an excellent way of bringing healing vibrations to the whole auric field. The guided visualization below can be recorded (but with the disclaimer that it is not to be used whilst driving or operating machinery) or read out by a friend, until it is memorised.

Chakra Colour Breathing Visualization

I want you to close your eyes and gradually become

aware of your breathing. Don't try to alter it in any way, just continue to breathe normally; in and out, in and out until you begin to feel peaceful, calm, and relaxed.

Pause 30 seconds

Now, I want you to take your mind down to your base chakra and, as you breathe in, I want you to visualize a powerful red light filling this energy centre with passion, determination and strength and, as you breathe out, I want you to release any feelings of anger, fear and negativity. Just continue to concentrate on this powerful red light as you breathe in and out, in and out.

Pause 30 seconds

Now, I want you to take your mind down to your sacral chakra and, as you breathe in, I want you to visualize a vibrant orange light filling this energy centre with creativity and an understanding of your closest relationships and, as you breathe out, I want you to release any feelings of blame, guilt or unhealthy control. Just continue to concentrate on this vibrant orange light as you breathe in and out, in and out.

Pause 30 seconds

Now, I want you to take your mind down to your solar plexus chakra and, as you breathe in, I want you to visualize a vivid yellow light filling this energy centre with confidence and self belief and, as you breathe out, I want you to release any feelings of inferiority, anxiety and worry. Now just continue to concentrate on this vivid yellow light as you continue to breathe in and out.

Pause 30 seconds

Now, I want you to take your mind down to your heart chakra and, as you breathe in, I want you to visualize a beautiful green light filling this energy centre with love, compassion and understanding and, as you breathe out, I want you to release any feelings of hatred, desolation and despair. Just continue to concentrate on this beautiful green light as you breathe in and out, in and out.

Pause 30 seconds

Now, I want you to take your mind down to your throat chakra and, as you breathe in, I want you to visualize a potent blue light filling this energy centre with decisiveness and self expression with which to realise your dreams and, as you breathe out, I want you to release any feelings of judgment or criticism towards yourself and others. Just continue to concentrate on this potent blue light as you breathe in and out, in and out.

Pause 30 seconds

Now, I want you to take your mind to your brow chakra and, as you breathe in, I want you to visualize a deep indigo light filling this energy centre with understanding and emotional intelligence and, as you breathe out, I want you to release any behaviours, which encourage you to deny who you really are. Just continue to concentrate on this deep indigo light as you breathe in and out, in and out.

Pause 30 seconds

Now, I want you to take your mind to your crown chakra and, as you breathe in, I want you to visualize a radiant violet light filling you with selflessness, courage and trust and, as you breathe out, I want you to release anything which suppresses your uniqueness in favour of following the thoughts of others. Just continue to concentrate on this radiant violet light as you breathe in and out, in and out.

Pause 30 seconds

Now it is almost time to bring yourself back to the reality of the room and as you do so, I want you to bring with you all that is positive and healing and leave behind all that no longer serves you well. Whenever you are ready you may open your eyes.

NB

As a simple precaution always ensure that if you make such a recording that you include within the early parts: '*Should my / your presence be required for any reason elsewhere then I / you will be able to attend to that in a safe and natural manner.*'

Dedication

For me, the sense of sight is symbolic of the element of water, for I am able to 'see' how others are feeling. I see their pain and their joy and it is also through this sense that I am able to enjoy the visual beauty of this fascinating world.

Sight enables me to enjoy the beauty of a mid-summer sunset, to look into my husband's eyes, to return a friend's smile, to take in the rugged beauty of Bodmin Moor, to watch the autumn leaves spin from their boughs, to see the promise in a rainbow, to read inspiring words, to wonder at the night sky and to appreciate the first snowfall of winter.

The following dedication to the goddess is an example of how we can express our appreciation for our sense of sight. Light a blue candle, symbolic of the throat centre, hopes, dreams and healing and place beside it an item that is pleasing to the eye, such as a painting or vase of flowers and chant the following dedication:

Lady Goddess gift bearer of the senses,
I appreciate and honour my sense of sight.
I give thanks that through sight I am able to rejoice in the splendour of the earth.
I give thanks that through sight I am able to look into the faces of my loved ones.
I give thanks that through sight I am able to heal and be healed through the vibrations of colour.
Please accept these flowers/ this painting as a token of my gratitude.

Let the candle burn right down if possible. It may be a generous gesture to give the flowers or painting to someone as a gift or take someone you care about to a place they would like to see.

Conclusion

The colours and images we choose to surround ourselves with through décor, clothes and food have a dramatic impact on our daily lives. It therefore becomes of the utmost importance that we choose shapes and colours which give us pleasure, thereby making us feel at peace in our environment, comfortable in our clothes and excited by the food on our plate.

Sunlight contains all the colours of the visible electromagnetic spectrum, making it necessary for our physical, emotional, psychological and spiritual well-being; therefore the more we venture out into natural daylight, especially in the winter, the better we will feel.

In the words of Jacob Liberman in his book *Light Medicine of the Future:* 'Colour has always been the thread that weaves us into the fabric of life, for all colour is light and light is life itself.'

Mrs Darley Tale: Rainbows of the Heart

'Here, let me help you carry something.'

I turned and saw Tamarind hurrying down the lane towards me as I piled up various laptops, briefcases and shopping bags onto the road beside my car.

'It's OK,' I called, 'I'm used to it.'

'Well that's no reason not to accept help,' she said as she stopped alongside me.

I returned her smile, once again wondering what it was about her that always made me feel so uncomfortable.

'You look tired,' she said looking into my eyes, 'mind you; I don't think that yellow blouse is doing you any favours if you don't mind me saying.'

'Oh,' I said, not quite knowing how to reply.

'I'm sorry,' she laughed, 'I didn't mean to sound so abrupt. It's just that I'm really into colour and how it affects the psyche. Look, why don't you come round after you've unpacked this lot and I'll tell you a bit more about it? I'll go and put the kettle on and it'll give us a chance to get to know each other a little better.'

I was on the verge of making a suitable excuse when I suddenly thought better of it, after all I had nothing to do, nowhere to go and, I thought, I might just learn something.

'OK,' I said, 'thanks. I'll be round in ten minutes.'

I had only been in Don's cottage briefly on a couple of occasions, but have to say that under Tamarind's influence the lounge was completely transformed.

'Wow!' I said as I stepped into what can only be described as a feast for the eyes.

'Do you like it?' She asked.

'Yes, yes I do. It's … well … colourful.' I said almost at a loss for words.

'I call it my rainbow room. It begins over here in the red corner, a place for restoring your flagging energy and,' she laughed, 'if the energy turns to passion, the chair reclines totally!'

I smiled, unsure as to whether she was joking as she turned her attention to the table covered with an orange cloth, which she referred to as her 'creativity desk' and so we went around the room as she explained each of the rainbow colours and what she used each area for.

'I'm fascinated,' I said, 'I had no idea that colour could affect us so dramatically.

'Oh, yes,' she said as she handed me a cup of what looked like a reddish coloured tea and carried with it a rather pungent aroma. 'Now you sit here in the red chair and drink that red bush tea and you'll begin to feel much livelier.'

The red-leafed tea gradually began to revive my spirits and, after chatting to Tamarind for a while about her beautiful, if rather unusual room, I finally found the courage to ask the question that had been bugging me.

'So what is it about my yellow blouse that is so awful?'

Tamarind laughed. 'It's not that it's awful, it just doesn't suit you. It drains you of colour and makes you look and, no doubt feel, washed out.'

'Well it's funny you should say that,' I said, 'I never feel at my best when I wear it and I only ever put it on when I've got nothing else and really need to do some ironing.'

'Exactly,' said Tamarind. 'You see, you don't really need yellow energy at the moment. Yellow is for mental stimulation and communication, something that you no doubt get in bucketfuls every day with your current job?'

I nodded.

'So, tell me, which colours make you feel good? Because those are the ones you should wear'

'Oh, I like pink and green; lilac too I suppose and my absolute favourite … black.'

'Oooo, that's a very telling foursome,' Tamarind said.

'Why?' I asked.

'Oh, don't look so worried,' she laughed. 'The colours you mentioned tell me that you would like to attract love into your life, that you crave balance between work and play, that you are searching for some spiritual meaning and, perhaps most importantly, that you sometimes feel vulnerable and would like someone to look after you. That's not to say though that you're not your own person, there's an inner strength in there. You know what you like and won't just accept anything or anyone in your life.'

Without warning and, much to my embarrassment, my eyes filled with tears and the room became distorted and blurred.

Within an instant, Tamarind had perched herself on the arm of my chair and pushed a tissue into my hand. 'Here,' she said. 'I didn't mean to upset you, it's just that colour speaks for itself. We can all say things that we think other people want to hear, but it's the things we don't say and the choices we make through our other senses that speak the loudest.'

I smiled through my tears. 'That's very true, in fact I'm renowned for saying what I think others want to hear. Mrs Darley has told me so on many occasions.'

'Ah, Mrs Darley,' said Tamarind. 'What a rare gem she is, always a wise answer for every situation. Mind you, it will be interesting to see how she's going to extricate herself from her present predicament.'

I looked at her questioningly.

'I'm referring to what she's going to do when her husband arrives on the scene.'

I sat for a moment, this new information spinning around my head. 'Husband?'

'Ah,' said Tamarind, 'you obviously didn't know.'

I shook my head. 'I thought he was dead.'

'Oh, dear, me and my big mouth again. Look, I didn't mean to speak out of turn, its just that you and Mrs D are so close and she often speaks of you with such affection that I presumed you knew ... that she would have said….' Tamarind's voice trailed off.

'Don't worry,' I said, 'I won't say anything to Mrs D, there's obviously some reason why she hasn't told me.'

'So you know then?' Mrs Darley asked me later that day as we stood waving Phyllis off down the lane.

'Know what?' I asked.

'About my second husband.'

I tried to avoid her gaze in the growing dusk and remained silent.

'It's OK, 'she said, 'Tamarind told me that she'd told you.'

'Oh,' I said, 'I wasn't going to say anything.'

'Why, for fear of upsetting me?' smiled Mrs Darley.

'Yes … no … well, for both of you really, Tamarind

wasn't talking out of turn, she thought I knew and so I said I wouldn't mention it.'

'That's no more than I would have expected,' said Mrs Darley, taking my arm and walking me back down the path. 'Holding your council as always, never rocking the boat, not wanting to upset the status quo and, perhaps for all those reasons, that's why I didn't tell you. But surely you didn't think I'd spent the last thirty three years alone in splendid isolation?'

I shook my head. 'No, of course not, but I still don't understand why you felt you couldn't tell me'

'Perhaps I didn't want to tell you because I didn't want to spoil the image you have of me, because I wasn't sure if you'd approve, because I wasn't sure whether you would understand. You see, my dear, there's a lot about me you have yet to discover.'

I looked at her as we reached her front door. 'Am I really so unapproachable? I asked, 'so perfect, so far removed from the realities of everyday life that you think I am totally without understanding, without human emotion?'

Mrs Darley shook her head. 'No, my dear, I don't, but because I didn't tell you at the outset, I somehow never seemed to find the right moment to rectify my omission and, when Tamarind came here, I remember you being slightly disapproving about her lifestyle, her free spiritedness, her lack of commitment and that confirmed to me that I had made the right decision.'

I sank down on her doorstep for what seemed like an eternity, only re-entering reality when she appeared from the kithen with a glass of hot whisky.

'What are you going to do? About Peter I mean,' I asked taking the glass from her and making room for her to join me.

She shook her head and stared into the darkness. 'In the near future I will have to make a decision and perhaps at that point I will feel more like talking about that aspect of my life. You see, my dear, in matters of the head versus the heart, there are no winners, for waiting in the wings is either the sharp knife of guilt or the dull pain of heartache.'

Forest Sunlight
Within the shaft, life is illuminated,
Secret, hidden until this moment.
Silvered threads of Arachne's daughters
Bind and weave the fabric of the woods.
Dewed jewels drip from fallen ferns,
Wounded pines weep resinous tears,
Midges dance with chaotic precision.
A vision; all but lost, if not for the light.

Chapter 9

Becoming Whole

Changes
I am fragmented,

A parent,
A spouse,
A child.

My mind, body and spirit
Dance alone,
Each unaware of the other's existence.

Change calls.

Mrs Darley Tale: The First Step
Having just lit my fire one foggy summer's evening, I was approached by Mrs Darley as I went to fill my coal bucket from the bunker.

'Hello, dear,' she said, 'It is chilly tonight isn't it, to say it's mid-June?'

I nodded. 'Yes, I thought the fog warranted a real fire rather than just putting the little convector heater on.'

'I'm inclined to agree, oh, and this is for you,' she said, handing me a large envelope. 'It needed a signature, so I took the liberty, I hope you don't mind.'

'No, I'm very grateful,' I said. 'It's saved me going down to the collection centre in Liskeard and, if it's what

I hope it is, you've cut down my waiting time.'

'How intriguing,' smiled Mrs Darley, 'I do hope it brings you the news you're expecting.'

'I'll let you know,' I said picking up my coal bucket and making my way back indoors.

Placing the envelope on the table, I made the fire and cooked myself a meal before allowing myself the luxury of opening it and reading the enclosed letter:

Dear Ms Carlton,

Thank you for your application to join the September course. We are delighted to offer you a place....

Mrs Darley smiled as she opened her door. 'Oh, hello, dear, come in, come in, I've taken a leaf out of your book and lit my fire too, in fact I was just about to settle beside it with a tot of whisky and the cheese board. Will you join me?'

'I'd love to,' I said as I entered the warmth of her cottage.

Mrs Darley disappeared into the kitchen and soon reappeared with a scrumptious cheese board which she placed on the little table between us.

'This looks lovely,' I said, 'thank you.'

'It's my pleasure,' she said, 'after all, I feel that perhaps a celebration may be called for.'

I laughed. 'Well, I think so and I wanted you to be the first one I shared the news with.'

'Then whatever it is, I'm honoured,' she said.

'I've been accepted on a course.'

'And what type of course might that be?' she asked.

'Aromatherapy and massage,' I replied.

'Well, well,' she smiled.

'I thought you'd be pleased to know that I do listen sometimes,' I said.

'As long as you've listened to your heart, my dear,' said Mrs Darley, 'and not simply to me, then I'm delighted for you.'

Meeting the Self

What is it, this desire to heal? Is it simply a desire to be well in the physical body and live as long as we can? Or is it through feeling the emotions, battling with the mind, knowing physical disorder and experiencing the dark night of the soul that we eventually come to understand the true meaning of healing and appreciate that life itself is a healing journey.

When we become ill, it becomes very easy to lose ourselves amid pain and fear and forget that our immediate experiences are part of a much bigger picture. In so doing, we allow our thoughts to be overwhelmed by negativity, whilst pushing positive vibrations further and further away. Over time, these thought patterns attract disease, making health little more than a remote possibility.

The universe is a neutral energy, providing us with what we focus on, therefore the more positive our intention, the more we attract positive vibrations and frequencies into our lives which, in healing terms, means health.

As the subconscious mind is unable to differentiate between what is real and what is imagined, we have to believe that we are on the pathway to healing, as this thought will attract healing energies towards us. The following quote from Philippians 4:8 encourages us to think in this way:

'Whatsoever things are true,
Whatsoever things are honest,
Whatsoever things are pure,
Whatsoever things are lovely,
Think on these things.'

Whenever we embark upon a journey of healing, regardless of whether it is physical, emotional, psychological or spiritual, we should make use of all the expertise available from doctors, healers, counsellors, psychiatrists and spiritual leaders, yet we should never underestimate the importance of our own contribution. Disease and disorder come as messengers and no matter what advice we may receive from significant others, only we are capable of understanding the message that our own body is trying to convey.

We must be silent, be still and journey within, via whichever medium we feel drawn to in order to hear the whisperings of our soul, for this is probably the most important journey we will ever make.

In the words of Katherine Dunham:

'Go within every day
And find your inner strength
So that the world will not blow your candle out.'

Mrs Darley Tale: The Shadow

'This year's charity jazz night is to be a masked ball instead!' gasped Phyllis as she struggled into Mrs Darley's cottage with an assortment of bags.

'Is it really, dear?' said Mrs Darley, 'how very exciting, but do come in and put all those things down before you tell us all about it.'

Having piled the table high with bags of various sizes,

Phyllis finally made herself comfortable in the fireside chair that I had just vacated in her honour.

'Sheila and Tony thought they'd do something a little different this year, having had a traditional jazz night for the past eight years or so and so they've decided on a masked ball, which Mike Rowse has kindly said they can hold in the hay barn at his farm over the other side of Minions.'

'Sounds great,' said Tamarind, 'any excuse for dressing up and getting theatrical, and, besides,' she added, 'there's nothing more exciting than no one knowing who you are. It all adds an air of mystery.'

'I quite agree,' said Mrs Darley. 'Behind a mask we can all be who we want to be, rather than who we think we should be.'

'Oooo,' laughed Rose, 'you make it sound quite risqué.'

'Well, in times past, I'm sure it was,' said Phyllis. 'Many a secret liaison was arranged from behind the perceived safety of a mask. I mean, back in the seventeenth century the upper classes were governed by the strictest social etiquette and the freedom a mask afforded from these stifling rules of behaviour must have been quite irresistible.'

'It also adds to the attractiveness factor,' said Tamarind. 'I remember being totally besotted with the Phantom of the Opera, simply because of his mask. He seemed remote somehow, forbidden even.'

'That's why affairs are so exciting,' said Mrs Darley, 'because we don't know the person behind the mask.'

'Mmmm,' murmured Rose, 'I've never thought about an affair in that way before, but you're quite right, it is the excitement of the unknown.'

'Of course,' said Mrs Darley, 'masks can also hide

our identity for other reasons than those of mere titillation. King Gustav III of Sweden was shot at a masked ball, an event played out in Verdi's opera'.

'Well let's hope there are no shootings at our ball,' laughed Phyllis. 'Anyway, who would like to see what's in the bags?'

To four enthusiastic 'me's, Phyllis walked over to the table and emptied out the bags from which tumbled an array of the most wonderful masks.

'Wow!' said Tamarind. 'These are beautiful, where did you get them?'

'Let's just say I was lucky enough to acquire them from an amateur operatic company, which was closing down when I lived in London. You are, of course, all at liberty to choose one each.'

With these words, Tamarind and Rose dived into the exotic pile of feathers and sequins whilst Phyllis turned to me.

'And which one catches your eye?' she asked.

'Oh, I'm not sure,' I said quickly, 'and anyway I don't know if I'll be around that weekend. Let the others choose theirs first.'

'Oh,' said Rose, 'look at this one, it's covered in tiny silk rose buds. It must have been made for me!'

'But that rather defeats the object of the exercise,' said Mrs Darley.

'Why?' Rose asked.

'Because the whole point of hiding behind a mask, is to enable your shadow side to emerge, to be who you truly are and yet are afraid to let others see. Carl Jung said that we all carry a shadow and the more we deny it, the darker it becomes and, the darker it becomes, the more likely we are to become ill.

'"*Between the conception and the creation, between*

the emotion and the response falls the Shadow",' murmured Phyllis.

'Quite,' said Mrs Darley, 'TS Eliot also appreciated the value of the shadow when he wrote those words in *The Hollow Men*. You see, the shadow is often linked to our more primal instincts and, due to the attitude of "respectable society" has, become repressed. However, that does not mean that it goes away, for it often manifests as a perceived shortfall in those with whom we come into contact.'

'What do you mean?' I asked.

'Well, a person may wish to be confident, outgoing, and sexually attractive, yet, for whatever reason, displays an outward persona that is anxious, quiet and plain, but rather than letting their shadow side out, they project their desired personality traits onto another and irrationally perceive that person to then have a moral shortfall.'

I nodded, realising that Mrs Darley and I had touched upon this subject once before when Tamarind came to live in our hamlet and I had made the judgement that she perhaps wasn't my type. I could now see that her attitude of living for the moment and having a sense of freedom and spontaneity were all elements which I would like to incorporate in my own life and yet, due to my need for control and my self imposed moralistic restrictions, I had constantly denied the existence of my own shadow.

'I've changed my mind,' I said suddenly turning to Phyllis, 'I would like to choose a mask, after all I can always change my weekend for going away.'

Phyllis was delighted and the next few minutes were spent with everyone holding up an array of masks accompanied by 'what about this one?' or 'try this.'

Eventually, having chosen an elegant silver mask

adorned with black feathers, the matter was finally settled and one by one we began to leave.

'So,' said Mrs Darley as I stood on her doorstep, 'why the sudden change of heart?'

'I think I've finally come to realise that in order for my life to work, I have to make changes and get to know who I really am instead of constantly living behind the mask.'

'Well, well,' said Mrs Darley, 'and how do you intend to do that?'

'You once said that you didn't think I was ready to join in your magickal gatherings because you thought I was afraid. And you were right, I was afraid. Afraid of what I would be opening myself up to, afraid of the unknown, afraid of my own shadow.'

'And now you're not?'

I shook my head. 'Oh, no, I am still afraid, but now I feel I'm ready to face those fears; to meet my shadow.'

Mrs Darley squeezed my hand.

'I want you to understand, my dear, that embarking upon this path will change your life and not all of the changes you encounter will feel comfortable.

'The journey of the spiritual warrior is not one that can be completed within a period of weeks or months, as there is much to learn and understand.

'It is certainly not a journey for the faint hearted. It takes time, practise, dedication and commitment to become adept in the magickal arts.'

'It's not a decision I've taken lightly,' I said, 'and I certainly don't expect it to be easy; nothing worth having ever is.'

'Then let the journey begin,' she said.

*****

Health

My suspicion I transform into trust,
My sadness to joy.
My despair I transform into hope,
My defeat to victory.

My criticism I transform into praise,
My self-doubt to belief.
My blame I transform into forgiveness,
My hatred to love.

My anger I transform into compassion,
My worry to understanding.
My sickness I transform into health,
My death into life.

Other Titles by Mirage Publishing

<u>Paperback Non-fiction Books</u>

A Prescription from The Love Doctor: How to find Love in 7 Easy Steps - Dr Joanne 'The Love Doctor' Coyle

Burnt: One Man's Inspiring Story of Survival - Ian Colquhoun

Cosmic Ordering Guide - Stephen Richards

Cosmic Ordering: Sex Energy - Stephen Richards

Cosmic Ordering: You Can be Successful - Stephen Richards

Hidden Secrets: Attract Everything You Want! – Carl Nagel

Internet Dating King's Diaries: Life, Dating and Love – Clive Worth

Life Without Lottie: How I survived my Daughter's Gap Year - Fiona Fridd

Forgiveness and Love Conquers All: Healing the Emotional Self - Stephen Richards

Mrs Darley's Moon Mysteries: A Celebration of Moon Lore and Magic – Carole Carlton

Mrs Darley's Pagan Elements: A Celebration of Air, Fire, Water, Earth and Divine Spirit – Carole Carlton

Mrs Darley's Pagan Whispers: A Celebration of Pagan Festivals, Sacred Days, Spirituality and Traditions of the Year – Carole Carlton

Rebel Diet: They Don't Want You to Have It! – Emma James

The Real Office: An Uncharacteristic Gesture of Magnanimity by Management Supremo Hilary Wilson-Savage - Hilary Wilson-Savage

The Tumbler: Kassa (Košice) – Auschwitz – Sweden - Israel - Azriel Feuerstein (Holocaust survivor)

Uncle Hitler: ***A Child's Traumatic Journey through Nazi Hell to the Safety of Britain*** – Alfred Nestor

Paperback fiction Books

I Can See Clearly Now The Rain Is Gone - George Korankye (This incorporates a factual event of the Dunblane massacre into a highly sensitive work of faction.)

AudioBooks

Inspire Me: Unlock Your Inner Happiness – Stephen Richards and Lisa Tenzin-Dolma

Cosmic Ordering AudioBook Series in *CD & MP3* format

Cosmic Ordering Connection - Stephen Richards
Cosmic Ordering: Chakra Clearing - Stephen Richards
Cosmic Ordering: Rapid Chakra Clearing – Stephen Richards
The Ultimate Cosmic Ordering Meditation– Stephen Richards
The Ultimate Cosmic Ordering Meditation - Stephen Richards

***Releasing you from* AudioBook series in CD & MP3 format**

Releasing You From Fear CD & MP3 - Stephen Richards
Releasing You From Insomnia CD & MP3 - Stephen Richards
Releasing You From Social Anxiety CD & MP3 - Stephen Richards
Releasing You From The Past - Stephen Richards

***The Ultimate* AudioBook series in CD & MP3 format**

The Ultimate 10 Minute Chakra Clearing - Stephen Richards
The Ultimate Change Your Life Guided Meditation - Stephen Richards
The Ultimate Confidence & Ego Boost CD & MP3 - Stephen Richards
The Ultimate Focus Builder - Stephen Richards
The Ultimate Inner Self Link Up - Stephen Richards
The Ultimate Power of Positive Thinking - Stephen Richards
The Ultimate Self Hypnosis CD & MP3 - Stephen Richards
The Ultimate Stop Smoking CD & MP3 - Stephen Richards
The Ultimate Success in Love CD & MP3 - Stephen Richards

The Ultimate Wealth Creation CD & MP3 - Stephen Richards
The Ultimate Weight Loss CD & MP3 - Stephen Richards

E-Books
7 Day Focusing Plan - Stephen Richards
Beating Procrastination - Stephen Richards
Boost Your Self Esteem - Stephen Richards
Forgiveness and Love Conquers All: Releasing You from the Past - Stephen Richards
FREE 7 Day Confidence & Ego-boost Affirmations - Stephen Richards
Releasing You From Self-limiting Beliefs - Stephen Richards
Supercharge Your Self-confidence – Stephen Richards
Think Your Way To Success - Stephen Richards